ECLIPSE

3/04

ECLIPSE

David and Carol Allen

ALLEN & UNWIN
Sydney   Wellington   London   Boston

First published in 1987
Allen & Unwin Australia Pty Ltd
8 Napier Street, North Sydney NSW 2060

Allen & Unwin New Zealand Ltd
60 Cambridge Terrace, Wellington, New Zealand

Allen & Unwin (Publishers) Ltd
Park Lane, Hemel Hempstead, Herts HP2 4TE England

Allen & Unwin Inc.
8 Winchester Place, Winchester Mass 01890 US

National Library of Australia
Cataloguing-in-Publication entry:
Allen, David A.
   Eclipse.

   ISBN 0 04 300095 9.

   1. Eclipses.   2. Eclipses—History.   3. Eclipses, Lunar.
   4. Eclipses, Solar.   I. Allen, Carol.   II. Title.

521′.8

Set in Garamond 3, Linotron 202 by Best-set Typesetter Ltd, Hong Kong
Printed in Hong Kong

Contents

Acknowledgements   vi
Illustrations   vii
1   Introduction   1
2   The sun   4
3   The moon   14
4   Eclipses of the moon   23
5   Only in transit   32
6   Eclipses of the sun   37
7   Astronomy and folklore   44
8   Ancient eclipse records   57
9   The mediaeval view   65
10 The golden age   73
11 Reminiscences of our first eclipse   93
12 Birds fell from the sky   99
13 Observing eclipses   110
Index   122

Acknowledgements

Permission to reproduce the following material is gratefully acknowledged.

Figures: 3.1 Anglo-Australian Observatory; 4.4 John Barton; 5.1 a+b Mitchell Library, Sydney; 6.3 High Altitude Observatory, Colorado (J.H. Rush et al.); 8.1 British Museum; 10.13 Master and Fellows of Trinity College, Cambridge; 10.1, 10.2, 10.3, 10.4, 10.5, 10.6, 10.7 and 12.1 Royal Astronomical Society; 13.2 Her Majesty's Stationery Office; *Plates*: 1 Observatoire de Paris; 3 and 4 Ron Royer; 7 Royal Astronomical Society; 9 Bob Cooper.

Illustrations

2.1	The sun	6
2.2	Observing the sun by projection	9
2.3	A solar projection screen	11
3.1	The moon	15
3.2	The period between new moons	18
4.1	Earth's shadow from a point source	25
4.2	Earth's shadow from the sun	25
4.3	Trajectories for lunar eclipses	27
4.4	Comet Halley during a lunar eclipse	28
4.5	Refraction of sunlight by the earth	30
5.1	Cook's record of the transit of Venus	35
6.1	Types of solar eclipse	38
6.2	Earth during 1988 solar eclipse	39
6.3	The solar corona at eclipse	42
6.4	Leaf shadows during an eclipse	43
7.1	Hatshepsut's obelisk	45
7.2	Casa Grande	47
7.3	Mayan glyphs	50
7.4	Stonehenge	51
7.5	The eclipses of a Saros cycle	54–5
8.1	Babylonian cuneiform tablet	63
10.1	Francis Baily	74
10.2	Baily's beads	75
10.3	Sir George Airy	76
10.4	1851 solar eclipse	78
10.5	1871 solar eclipse	80
10.6	Two drawings of the 1874 solar eclipse	81
10.7	Equipment for the 1878 eclipse	82
10.8	Observers in Spain, 1900	85
10.9	Expedition dress	86
10.10	Expedition of 1908	87

10.11	Expedition of 1911	88
10.12	Eclipse clock, 1911	89
10.13	Arthur Eddington	90
10.14	The bending of light around the sun	90
11.1	Softening shadows before an eclipse	95
11.2	The diamond ring effect	97
12.1	Shadow bands	100
12.2	Spanish parade, 1900	107
13.1	Two moonscapes	111
13.2	1988 eclipse track	119

Colour plates lie between pages 56–7 and 72–3.

1	The 1724 solar eclipse over Paris
2	A telescope on Mauna Kea
3	A lunar eclipse
4	A triple exposure of a lunar eclipse
5	Total solar eclipse—wide-angle view
6	Total solar eclipse, in detail
7	Drawing of the 1851 solar eclipse
8	The earth shadow
9	A partial solar eclipse at sunset

Introduction 1

The sky above our heads is at once beautiful and mysterious. Its beauty is there for all to see—the towering head of a thunder cloud tinged pink and gold by the setting sun; the sweep of a bright comet on the blackness of night; the arch of a rainbow, pastel against a leaden backdrop. The mystery of the sky is reserved only for the curious, for those who look beyond the ephemeral vistas to ask why? how? when?

This book examines just one facet of that celestial panorama: the eclipse. Eclipses of the sun, eclipses of the moon—phenomena that are no more in reality than a simple manifestation of the timeless mechanics of the universe, a rhythmic dance undertaken by three small and insignificant bodies in one of its lesser corners. The book looks at their beauty, sketches some of the history of man's view of them, and examines them from the scientist's standpoint.

It is the celestial event which comes naturally to mind when the word eclipse is used, but the meaning is somewhat broader, and it is instructive to trace the etymology. The word derives from the Greek *ex-leipsis*, which translates to mean 'leaving its place', hardly a direct reference to the celestial phenomenon. In Latin it became *eclipsis*, from which our modern word derives. English as we know it today evolved from Latin and Saxon roots, but a work dated 1300 AD refers to 'exlepsis of sun and mone', which seems to show that the Greek influence also existed in this case. On the other hand, mediaeval spelling was not altogether reliable: witness the phrase from 1485 'the sun has lost his sight; eclipped was hee.'

The word ellipsis keeps more closely to the original Greek in meaning, and refers to the omission of words which are deemed unnecessary. The triple ellipsis (. . .) is used in some of the quotations given in this book where former writers seemed to the present authors unnecessarily verbose.

The word eclipse has other meanings besides the astronomical. The Oxford English Dictionary catalogues half a dozen, one of which is 'a fraudulent manoeuvre in dice playing.' The remainder share a common theme however, and between these the distinction is fine. Samuel Johnson, commenting on the death of the great actor David Garrick, used one meaning: 'I am disappointed by that stroke of death, which has eclipsed the gaiety of nations . . .'. Sir Douglas Mawson, Australian Antarctic explorer, described the winds in Adelie Land as 'so terrific as to eclipse anything previously known in the world'. Benjamin Disraeli, Prime Minister of Great Britain last century, commented that we should 'sing in a room or the nightingale would eclipse us'. An earlier usage dates from 1577 when an historian named Holinshead referred to 'the eclipsed state of England' following the death of King Edward. Dryden, in 1662, had a milder meaning in mind when he wrote 'I confess I was a little eclipsed, but I'll cheer up'.

A derivative of the word is the 'ecliptic', the path followed by the sun across the background star fields. Instead of being named after the sun itself, the ecliptic became recognised as the great circle joining places where eclipses of the sun could occur. Such was the impact of these events on early scientific and popular thought.

Eclipses of the sun and moon are events displayed solely for the eyes of folk here on Earth. An astronaut on the moon, for example, would see no eclipses of the Earth, whilst those of the sun would be singularly boring affairs, in marked contrast to our view.

In any year at least two eclipses occur. The greatest number possible is seven, and four is typical. From any point on the Earth's surface rather fewer than half are visible, so unless you are prepared to travel a fair distance around the circumference of the globe you will see only one or two eclipses per year. Of course, this number may possibly be reduced even further: it may be cloudy!

Nonetheless, most of us have seen an eclipse, at least of the moon. The media tends to publicise eclipses when they occur, but they do not, however, answer all the questions that the curious might ask. Large astronomical tomes provide detailed answers, whereas this book gathers together just the information the inquisitive might ask in connection with eclipses. More than that, it delves into the rich historical literature on the subject—the myths and legends, the verse, the anecdotes; even the prehistoric view that archaeologists have shown us.

The authors have one further aim in writing this book: to bring to your attention one of Nature's most magnificent events. Witnessed by few, total eclipses of the sun cannot but stir the spectator's emotions. They are experiences that defy a full description (though many, including the present authors, foolishly try to give one), and events that all should endeavour to witness at least once if they are to deem their experience of life complete.

The book begins with a brief description of the dramatis personae, the sun and the moon. It would be difficult indeed to conceive of a two-act play in which the actors have such different personalities.

But first to explain the quotation at the head of this brief chapter. 'Eclipse' was the name given to one of the most famous of English racehorses, who was foaled in 1764. In an eighteen month period between 1769 and 1770 he ran in 15 races and remained unbeaten. So outstanding was this horse, whose skeleton now resides at the Royal Veterinary College in London, that in 1884 a regular race was inaugurated at Sandown Park named the Eclipse Stakes. The quotation has come into common parlance to refer to anyone who far outstrips their rivals, especially in sporting activities.

2 The sun

The sun whose rays are all ablaze
With ever-living glory.
GILBERT AND SULLIVAN,
The Mikado

On a moonless night, in a country area well distant from city lights, several thousand stars can be seen. The stars are faint pinpricks of light etched into a sooty background, and it is easy to visualise them as small, luminous objects like miniature electric light bulbs mounted on the interior of a black sphere that spins slowly above our planet. This impression can be heightened by a visit to a planetarium, for there the stars are merely spots of light projected onto the dark interior of a dome.

The myriad stars we see represent a minuscule fraction of the whole galaxy of stars in which we live—the Milky Way Galaxy. For those who collect superlatives, astronomers have estimated that about one hundred thousand million stars inhabit our Galaxy, a figure comparable to the number of grains of rice one might pack into any of our largest public buildings. The Galaxy is, however, mostly empty. If we were to scale the Galaxy down so that a typical star was no larger than a grain of rice, then we should have to scatter the grains about 100km from one another in order to represent our region of the Galaxy accurately.

Our night-time scene is typical of views within the Galaxy—blackness pierced by the rarity of starlight. Our daytime view contrasts with this. Pre-eminent in the sky, the sun outshines the brightest stars by a factor of ten thousand million, dazzling us and drowning all else. Yet the sun is just an average star, special in no way, unless we argue that our presence gives it significance. If we were to place ourselves in the model where stars are scaled down to grains of rice, we would be a mere 15cm distant from the grain that represents the sun, a figure that should be compared to the 100km between rice grains. No wonder then, that our sun so dominates our astronomical scene.

The rice-grain analogy may scale the sun and its environment to something we can comprehend, but it is grossly misleading. The size of stars, and the distances between them, are immense almost beyond comprehension. The sun, our star, is more than one million kilometres across, fully one hundred times the diameter of our earth. A journey to the sun, non-stop at the speed of a jet aircraft, would require two full decades. It is a greater distance than any earth-bound creature, even a member of an airline crew, can ever hope to cover. Astronauts, zipping round the earth once every one and a half hours, still need 8 months to clock up the distance between the earth and the sun.

Stars are the basic building blocks of the Universe, congregating together into galaxies. Some stars are bigger than the sun, perhaps as much as one or two hundred times its weight; some are as little as one twentieth its bulk. Some are hotter than the sun, shining a blue-white hue in contrast to the sun's yellow; others are cool and dull red in colour. To know our sun is only to begin to know stars. Because of its proximity, we believe we know our sun rather well.

Whereas on earth we can set our feet on terra firma, or bob about in the water for relaxation, neither option would be open to us if we could visit the sun. Just like the air we breathe, the sun is entirely gas from its outermost surface to the very core. Indeed, the gaseous state is the norm throughout the universe; our earth, indeed ourselves, are exceptional.

In the youthful universe, some 10 000 million years ago, the gas that now forms our sun was extremely tenuous. Since then the force of gravity has caused the gas cloud to shrink, growing denser in a number of locations. Over the millennia, these regions separated into collapsing clouds, each eventually to become a star. Within each cloud, the gas was to grow hotter, a natural consequence of shrinking. The shrinkage occupied some thousands of millions of years, a timescale typical of astronomical activities. Yet at one brief instant an extraordinary event occurred. The temperature within the cloud became high enough for some of its constituent atoms to fuse together; this fusion liberated energy, warming the gas further. More fusions occurred. Within hours a natural hydrogen bomb was formed at the centre of the gas cloud. Hydrogen was the most abundant element within the gas from which the sun was made, and the fusion converted it to helium, a process which continues today, and which liberates energy in impressive amounts. This is the mechanism that causes the sun to shine.

Scientists of last century pondered over the sun and stars. It was relatively simple to calculate how much energy the sun releases—the figure is 380 000 000 000 000 000 000 000 kilowatts every second. It is also fairly easy to calculate the sun's mass—a mere 2 000 000 000 000 000 000 000 000 tonnes. The only heat-emitting activities known to scientists last century were chemical, as when wood burns in our hearth. The most efficient burning scheme known would, for an object as massive as the sun, maintain so prodigious an output for only a few thousand years. Yet geological evidence clearly pointed to the sun having shone on the earth for many millions of years. The dilemma was profound, and led to heated exchanges between astronomers and geologists.

Around the turn of the century, the foundations of modern physics were laid with the quantum theory of the atom and Einstein's theory of relativity. Astronomers began to realise that there were ways of getting *more* energy out of simple substances, and that although they had not yet mastered the techniques, Nature had been doing the job for as long as time itself, in each and every one of those twinkling stars.

Armed with the new physics, astronomers were able to upwardly revise their estimate of how long the sun could shine, to ten thousand million years. At present, the sun is about half way through its fuel, and thus its lifetime.

The fusion of hydrogen occurs only in the hottest place, at the centre of the sun. There the temperature is an incomprehensible 200 million degrees Celsius. Further out the temperature falls, and at the surface is a meagre 5400°C, still hot enough not only to melt but to evaporate all known substances. It is because of the high temperatures that the sun can contain nothing but gas.

When the nuclear fusion began, an outward force was established by the energy rushing to the surface. The sun underwent a brief settling-down adolescence before attaining its present size. The shrinkage ceased, radiation balanced gravity, and the sun resigned

2.1   The sun, our daytime star, is the only source of light within the solar system.

itself to a stable life. It remains essentially the size and temperature it was five thousand million years ago.

Although gas is normally tenuous material, the enormous weight of the sun causes the inner parts to be highly compressed. Gas it still is, because of the temperature, but at its heart the sun is denser than steel. The average density of the entire sun slightly exceeds that of water.

Because the heat is generated near the centre, the sun is continually churning over. Like jam on the boil, pockets of warm material rise, cool, and in turn sink back below new portions. Unlike jam, however, the rising and falling material is gas, and the portions are the size of terrestrial continents. As these pockets of gas rub against one another, the friction creates more heat, with the result that the surface of the sun is actually warmer than the gas a few thousand kilometres down.

The surface we see is not really the outer boundary of the sun. It is a place where the change of gas density with height is very rapid, but it is not a change of state. The sun has an atmosphere which merges into the fiery disc we see; this is in contrast to the earth's crust which differs from the air above it. The use of the terms 'surface' and 'atmosphere' on the sun is misleading. We can gain some idea of the situation if we contemplate a bird's-eye view of dense fog. Looking down, the bird may think it sees a surface, but actually sees only an ill-defined level where the fog has become opaque. An object deeper in the fog is invisible; one higher up can be seen. There is no solid surface: the density of the fog merely becomes less as one rises through it. In the same way, the apparent surface of the sun is merely the level at which its gas is opaque as seen from above.

Higher than this apparent surface the gas is very tenuous indeed—so much so that we cannot see it except during a total eclipse. We can, nevertheless, define and measure the temperature. Surprisingly, the temperature continues to rise for a considerable distance above the sun, because of the friction generated by the rising and falling streams of gas. In the sun's outer atmosphere, a place known as the corona, the temperature reaches two million degrees.

Many fascinating phenomena are associated with the sun. Here it is important to describe only two of them—sunspots and prominences; the former because they are relatively easy to see, and the latter because they are relevant to the subject of eclipses.

Although sunspots are prominent dark blotches on the sun, rather few people have actually observed them because the sun is so very bright. Indeed, it is essential that all observations of the sun, whether of eclipses or sunspots, be undertaken with care to avoid the risk of severe eye damage.

The sun is bright enough that when focused through a small magnifying glass it can char and ignite paper or dry grass. The front of our eyes are small magnifying glasses that focus whatever we look at onto one of the most vital and delicate of our organs, the retina. The eye is remarkably adaptive. It can function in the blackest of environments, eventually adjusting to the merest glimmer of light. At the other end of the range it can handle full daylight with relative comfort. It cannot, however, adapt to or recover from being burnt. Every time you stare at the sun for longer than a second or two you destroy a small part of your retina, and hence of your vision. Irreparably. Moral: *Never stare at the sun.*

Telescopes and binoculars are devices that make a scene both bigger and brighter. Looking at the sun through a telescope or binoculars is a way of destroying a larger patch of your eye faster. *Never even glance at the sun through a telescope or binoculars.*

There are, however, a few occasions when it is safe to look directly at the sun. When it is low in the sky, seen through fog or smoke, and dull red, it can feel comfortable to the eye. Viewing is then quite harmless, provided that the smoke isn't going to clear suddenly.

It is also safe to view the sun through filters, provided that they are very dark. Sunglasses are not dark enough. The filter should be so dark that you can barely see a normal 100-watt light through it. An easily-made filter comprises one or two layers of black-and-white film that have been overexposed and developed. The old idea of making a filter by blackening glass in a smoky candle flame is less reliable because it rarely gives a uniform cover: the waving hand or head might bring a thin spot in front of the eye. Filters should never be used just behind the eyepiece of a telescope either: there they receive a concentrated blast of sunlight, and can crack or melt without warning.

Sunspots visible to the unaided eye are rather rare, and if one is to see them regularly, one needs an instrument. The simplest instrument is easy to make. Choose a dark room with heavy curtains or blinds. At a sun-facing window mount a piece of card with a small pinhole in it, taking care not to let sunlight enter the room by any other route. You

2.2 a-c   Steps in projecting an image of the sun using a small pair of binoculars.
a   Mount the binoculars on a tripod or other firm but adjustable support. Ensure that one of the lenses is covered. Stand them in sunlight very near the edge of a shadow from a building.
b   Tilt the binoculars, watching their shadow on a nearby piece of paper, until they are lined up with the sun. A bright, fuzzy spot will appear in the shadow.
c   The bright spot is an image of the sun which can now be projected back onto a more distant piece of paper to make it larger. This image can be made sharp by adjusting the focus of the binoculars. Surrounding the final image by a suitable shade will improve the contrast.

a

b

c

have then made a pinhole camera. A shaft of sunlight will pass through the pinhole to make a small image of the sun. The diameter of that image will be roughly one centimetre for every metre of distance behind the pinhole. Unless the room is big and the sun low in the sky, you must be content with an image only two or three centimetres across. In that case your pinhole should be no bigger than a millimetre in diameter, otherwise you will see sunspots no better than with the unaided eye. Unfortunately, very small pinholes don't let through much light. Experiment with different holes to find the smallest you can use while still seeing the sun well, and try to improve the blacking-out of the room to make the sun's image easier to see.

For a better view you need a telescope, or a pair of binoculars with one lens covered over. You also need a steady hand or, better still, a tripod. Figures 2.2 a-c illustrate stages in the procedure.

Site yourself near to some deep shade such as a building, but obviously keep the telescope in the sunlight. The trick is to point the telescope at the sun without looking through it. Do this by tilting the telescope until its shadow is a circle. When correctly aligned, a bright spot will appear near the middle of the shadow. By slightly swinging the telescope you can move the circle of light into the shadow of the building. Angle the circle onto a piece of white paper that faces the telescope, and focus the telescope until the circle has sharp edges. The circle is then an image of the sun. Look for small, dark spots that move around with the image as you wobble the telescope or paper. It is fairly rare to find that there are no spots on the sun big enough to be seen by this, the so-called projection technique.

Spots on the sun are not manifestations of some terrible malaise, but the normal response of the gases to the various forces they encounter. One particular force is that of magnetism—the same force that swings a compass needle. Whereas on earth the needle inevitably points towards one of the two magnetic poles, on the sun the magnetic force is highly contorted by the ever-swirling gas. A hypothetical compass carried round on the sun would point every conceivable way, including up and down.

In places where the compass points vertically, hollows form in the sun's surface, hollows in the sense that we can see deeper in, to the cooler gas. Cooler in turn means darker, hence the spot. Sunspots are actually intensely bright areas which appear dark only because they are embedded in even brighter material.

Spots form and dissipate, lasting anything from a day to a month or more. Bigger spots usually last longer. They are carried round as the sun rotates, taking about 4 weeks to complete one circuit. The rotation of the sun can be monitored by daily observations of sunspots using the projection method. Simply project the sun into an appropriate circle drawn on the piece of white paper, and mark the position of all spots visible. The home handyman can make this job easier by building a projection screen on the back of a tripod-mounted telescope, as shown in Figure 2.3. It is advisable to make the observation always at about the same time of day or confusion can arise, because the sun appears at different orientations throughout the day.

The number of spots on the sun ranges enormously through a cyclic pattern lasting about 11 years. The sun was spottiest around 1979, and should be again in 1990. Roughly midway between the dates of maximum spottiness, the number of spots can be lower by a factor of five or ten. The exact number of spots is not predictable, however. There are longer term changes too, such as a period in the 17th century when spots disappeared altogether for about 70 years; this period is known as the Maunder minimum, after an English astronomer who will feature later in this book.

Chinese observers many centuries ago recorded spots on the sun, even though it is often claimed that Galileo discovered them with his telescope in 1609. A German chronicler named Einhard, reported

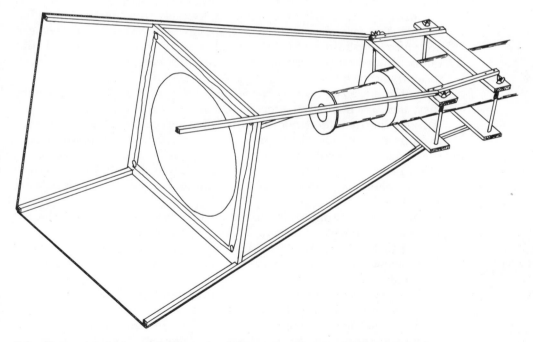

2.3   For regular viewing of the sun, a simple box can be constructed. Note the use of tracing paper, or kitchen greaseproof paper, as a screen. For clarity, two of the plywood sides are shown removed. A black cloth must be snugly wrapped around the junction of the frame and the telescope.

what must have been a sunspot throughout one week in March 807, so Galileo cannot even claim the first European sighting. From the Chinese records we can suspect that there were other long periods during which spots ceased altogether on the sun, but of course the Chinese saw only the very largest of them, so we have no knowledge of how many smaller ones persisted through the barren years. The Chinese had the potential to discover that the sun rotates from watching the spots from day to day, but they appear not to have made the deduction.

In contrast to sunspots, prominences are brighter than their environs, and are regions where hot gas has been drawn up to a greater altitude. They cannot be seen against the sun's disc without the use of special instruments, and are most easily viewed during total eclipses when they resemble pink flames projecting from the sun. The pink hue is caused by hydrogen gas which glows with a characteristic colour, much as salt tossed into a candle flame burns orange due to its sodium content.

The region immediately above the apparent surface of the sun, where the gas is transparent, itself glows the same hydrogen pink, and is called the chromosphere, from the Greek word *chromos* meaning colour. The chromosphere is very shallow, however, so can be seen only for an instant as a total eclipse begins or ends. The prominences can be thought of as portions of the chromosphere dragged further out so as to be more easily seen.

Prominences are usually associated with sunspots because, again, they appear when the magnetic pull is vertical. For reasons that are still only partly understood, the turbulent sun can toss globs of gas out from its surface. The gas streams along the magnetic field, rising from the surface but sometimes circling back down again at another spot. Prominences have been seen to extend to extraordinary distances, their heights being measured in tens or hundreds of thousands of kilometres.

The sun's complex magnetic field also distorts the corona, generating lengthy plumes and rays. Perhaps this corona, seen only during a total eclipse, gave rise to the winged sun god of Egyptian, Persian and Hittite mythology that has been handed down to us as the sunburst.

We have come a long way in our understanding of the sun since the Persians and Egyptians first worshipped it. In the fifth century BC the Greek scientist Anaxagoras argued that the sun was a red hot ball of metal greater in width than the Peloponnesus (110 miles or 180km). For the blasphemy of studying matters cosmic, Anaxagoras stood trial; yet he foreshadowed the great scientific movement in Greece whose traditions we still follow.

To recap: the sun we see is a dense ball of very hot gas continuously powered by a vast, natural hydrogen bomb. In the time it took you to read this chapter, the sun consumed a quantity of hydrogen comparable in mass to a major range of mountains. Yet its reservoir of gas is so great that it will shine uninterrupted for a further 5000 million years.

3 The moon

The minde of men chaungeth as the mone.
STEPHEN HAWES, c. 1520

The moon looks different from the sun in three ways. It is fainter, giving at best one millionth of the sun's light (20 stops in photographic parlance); it has permanent markings; and, most importantly, it exhibits phases.

The phases of the moon demonstrate that it does not shine by its own light but only basks in sunlight. Just as for us on earth, the moon has a sunlit day hemisphere and a dark night hemisphere. The moon takes slightly over four weeks to spin once on its axis, in contrast to the 24 hours earth requires. It also happens that the moon takes the same time to circle the earth. The combination of these two identical rotation periods ensures that the moon always keeps the same side turned our way.

During each lunar month we can watch the terminator—the line dividing night and day hemispheres—progress across the grey-white disc. For any place on the moon, the day lasts two weeks, as does the night. Because the terminator runs completely round the moon, we see one half of its perimeter between new and full moon, and the other half from full back to new. In the first half of the lunation, the sun is rising on the landscape and we call this the sunrise terminator. After full moon, we watch the progress of sunset.

If, on a given date, a narrow crescent is illuminated, then two weeks later the same narrow crescent will be dark, and the remainder sunlit. In each four week period the moon progresses once round the sky relative to the sun. Because we count time by the sun, our clocks show the moon rising and setting later each day, by an average of about 50 minutes: after fours weeks it has progressed through the full 24 hours. Thus two weeks after seeing the crescent moon, one must look 12 hours later or earlier in the day to see the corresponding gibbous moon with its dark crescent.

Within the solar system only the sun emits light. All other bodies

14

THE MOON.

3.1   The lifeless world of the moon is a study in black and white. © Anglo–Australian Observatory.

are lit by the sun and bounce the light back to us. If seen from a suitable vantage, all would show phases. An observer on the moon would see the earth's phases exactly as we see the moon's, requiring the same four weeks to complete each cycle. Our moon-bound observer could also watch the earth spinning round every 24 hours, and would see familiar landmarks go into or come out of darkness.

This restless circling of astronomical bodies merits an explanation.

15

First, all bodies spin about an axis. There is very little friction in space to slow down that rotation—an object that starts spinning will continue to do so almost for ever. All objects start off spinning because the gas clouds of the universe are all rotating, albeit incredibly slowly. When a cloud condenses, its rotation is speeded up according to fundamental laws of physics.

In practice the earth is slowing down in its rotation. We see the friction that slows it whenever we watch waves crash onto a beach or headland. The tides in our oceans drag on the earth as it rotates underneath them. It takes much energy to push a continent through the hump of high tide, hence the slowing. Scientists who monitor the earth's rotation have measured the lengthening of the day. Few years go by now without a 'leap second' being introduced. The sequence of one-second time pips on New Year's Eve then runs 23h 59m 58s ... 59s ... 60s ... 00h 00m 00s ... 01s ... 02s ... Normally, of course, 23h 59m 60s does not exist. Leap seconds are also sometimes added on June 30. This does not mean that every year the day is getting longer by a second. The leap second is a single correction made because the earth has run slightly slow over a year, and not a change to the length of every day. One leap second in a year means that the earth has lost 1/365 of a second each day, compared to the length of day calculated early in this century.

Objects also must orbit about one another. If they did not, they would be pulled together by the force of gravity just as the apocryphal apple, when released from its branch, was pulled downwards till it collided with Newton's head. The act of orbiting about the pulling body simulates a balancing force. We can sense the outward pull when we swing an object round our hand. The faster we spin it, the stronger the pull. To compensate for the sun's gravitational pull, which is a million times stronger than the earth's, planets must orbit the sun. Because the pull of gravity becomes weaker the further one recedes from the sun, the more distant planets do not have to hurry so much to be in balance. Mercury, only four tenths of earth's distance from the sun, takes just 88 days to make one circuit. At the other extreme, Pluto can spend nearly 250 of our years on each orbit. As an old Australian bush song, by the inimitable Anon, expresses it:

The earth rolls on through empty space, its journeys never done,
It's entered for a starry race throughout the Kingdom Come.
And as I am a bit of earth, I follow it because—
And prove I am a rolling stone and never gather moss.

The moon orbits the earth for the same reason. It is a great deal closer to the earth than any planet is to the sun, but the lesser gravity of the earth allows the moon to take 27.2 days to make each circuit. The moon does not follow a perfectly circular path round the earth: its distance changes by about 5 per cent either side of the average. Its closest approach is called perigee, and its most distant apogee. The time between perigees is nearly 27.6 days.

The interval between new moons is longer, however. Figure 3.2 illustrates this effect. At A the moon is new, lying between the earth and the sun. One orbit later the direction from earth to moon remains the same, but the earth has moved round the sun to position B. In order to be new once again, the moon must move a bit further. The average period between new moons is about 29.5 days. The period between full moons is, of course, the same.

An important corollary of this complex motion, for the purpose of this book, is that the moon is not at the same distance from earth every time it is new. It therefore varies in apparent size from one new moon to the next, being largest when new moon coincides with perigee. It takes 13½ months for the apparent size of the new moon to go through a complete cycle from large to small and back to large.

There remains to be explained the interesting fact that the moon keeps the same face turned earthwards. The reason is disarmingly simple. The moon is not perfectly round: it bulges on one side, by about 0.5km. The earth's gravity pulls that bulge and forces it to stay as close as it can be—on the front face. Because the moon keeps only one face turned our way, so the earth stays in the same spot in the lunar sky. Observers on the moon see the earth all the time, or not at all, according to whether or not they are on the hemisphere with the bump. Experts reading this section may complain that some minor wobbles of the moon's apparent motion have been ignored, but these are of no consequence to the basic theme.

From the face of the moon we see, earth is, of course, visible. Around new moon, when the sun has set on the face of the moon which is turned our way, the earth is fully lit up. It appears four times as large in the lunar sky as does the moon to us, and reflects light much better than the moon. So the earth gives the moon more than one hundred times the light that the moon gives the earth. You can sometimes see the earthlight on the moon when it is a narrow crescent in the twilight sky. The dark part of the moon glows very dimly, a phenomenon known popularly as 'the old moon in the new moon's arms.'

The permanent markings on the moon tell us that it is not a gaseous body like the sun, but has a rigid understory just like the earth. More-over, the moon has none of the clouds that make the earth an ever-changing kaleidoscope. Despite its lack of clouds, early astronomers wanted the moon to resemble the earth they knew, and so convinced themselves that the dark areas were sheets of water. The error of this

17

3.2 When the moon is new it lies between earth and sun. After one orbital revolution the moon will occupy the same direction in space as seen from the earth. Because the earth has progressed around the sun, the moon must travel a little further to become new once again. The drawing is not to scale.

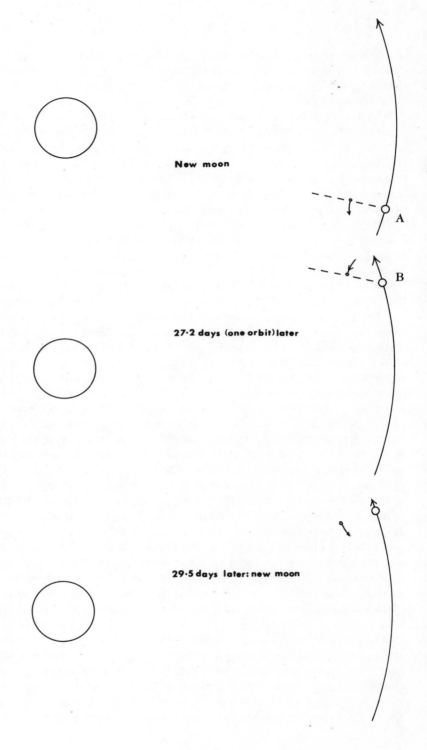

New moon

A

B

27·2 days (one orbit) later

29·5 days later: new moon

18

belief became apparent when it was realised that we should see a reflection of the sun off an ocean, and none was ever seen. Nonetheless, the dark features retain to this day Latin names enshrining the old belief as follows:

Mare = sea, Oceanus = ocean, Sinus = bay.

Now, of course, man has been to the moon. A dozen men have left a litter of metal scraps there. They plastered their footprints on its virgin soil, and carted off souvenirs from its hitherto untouched surface. All in the name of science, we are told. In the course of this petty vandalism, man has learnt a great deal about the moon—much too much to be related here, but some of it worthy of mention.

Let the comparison with the sun be carrried a little further. The moon is cold and solid, whilst the sun is hot and gaseous. Yet both were formed by the same process, the gradual shrinkage of a tenuous cloud of gas. What caused such different outcomes? Quite simply, size. The moon is a very tiny body, a miniature planet. Its diameter is barely one quarter that of the earth, its mass little more than one per cent. One hundred million moons would pack into the sun and still leave space for more.

Here we have the quintessential difference between stars and planets. When a gas cloud collapses to form a planet-sized body, it never becomes hot enough for nuclear reactions to occur. The very processes that make starlight cannot function. Planets can be thought of as failed suns.

The story is more complicated, however. The moon, and indeed all the planets that orbit our sun, did not form at the same time as the star. Instead, when the sun was made, some small percentage of the gas failed to become part of it. This gas was spinning round the sun too fast to fall in, and so spread itself out into a flattish disc, a fluffy pancake of material surrounding the fledgling star. From the gas within that pancake condensed uncountable numbers of minuscule grains of sand, smaller even than the finest grains on any beach you know. The grains began to jostle one another and to stick together, so that gradually big lumps of rock formed at the expense of the smaller ones. Bigger and bigger they grew, until in time the pancake was cleared almost completely of gas and dust, and became transformed into a whirling avalanche of sand, rocks and boulders. From this mêlée grew the earth, the moon, and the planets.

Now we see these bodies for what they really are. They are merely the dregs left over from making the sun, and no more significant than the thinnest smear of cake mix left in the bowl when the cake itself is in the oven and the children have extracted all the scrapes they can. This earth that is our home, and that seems so important to us, is utterly inconsequential in the scheme of the universe. The moon is an even lesser body. Yet by a curious quirk of Nature, the sun and moon appear of similar size in our skies, and play not grossly dissimilar roles in our lives.

The build up of rocks to make our moon was not a gentle process. Those rocks, some bigger than mountains, collided at speeds measured in kilometres per second. Each collision made a mighty crash, and each collision also helped to warm the moon as the energy of motion was converted to heat. Over the thousand million years or so that this process required, the moon warmed sufficiently to become molten deep within. The heat escaped through the surface in the form of small volcanoes, and quite extensive lava flows issued from fissures in the rock. The so-called lunar seas were indeed once liquid: they were oceans of molten rock that oozed from cracks in the surface, spread out across the shallow plains, then cooled and solidified. Over the intervening aeons the very rock has crumbled to black dust, dust that would be one of the most fertile soils we know if only it had water. Dust that is also one of the blackest of all materials, not much brighter than soot.

Volcanoes were not, however, the primary agents that shaped the moon. It was the impacting rocky debris that pocked and scarred its surface, making the famous craters which we view through a telescope. The basins that filled with molten rock are themselves giant craters, some up to 1000km in diameter; the collisions that produced such gigantic pocks must have been dramatic—nearly violent enough to rend the moon apart.

The earth was made by the selfsame process. Earth grew big enough to retain oceans and atmosphere, whereas on the moon both would quickly escape to space. Earth also retains volcanoes, and experiences earthquakes and the related phenomenon of continental drift, whereas the moon is now cold and virtually dead. Water, wind, volcanic action, earth movements, glaciers, vegetation—all modify the surface of our planet. They have transformed it from a cratered battleground into the world we know. The moon is a cameo of what the earth looked like some four thousand million years ago.

The malleable, molten interior of the earth allows its outer crust to readjust when necessary. Mountains don't last long, at least not by the standards of geological time. Relatively recently the Indian sub-continent has been rafted northwards from its original home adjacent to Antarctica. India collided with Asia, wrinkling the earth's surface to make the Himalayan Mountains that rise 8000 metres above the plains. The Himalayas are still rising, as India hasn't quite been halted, but they will not rise much higher. Beneath the enormous weight of the Himalayas, the earth is deforming. A few million years from now the Himalayas will have subsided considerably: mountains of that height are relatively rare.

On the moon, where only a tiny central portion was ever molten, mountains have survived from the time of their formation. There are mountains on the moon, encircling some of the craters, that rise higher above the plains than the loftiest peaks of the Himalayas, despite their great antiquity of some four thousand million years. The bulge that locks the moon to turn always the same face to earth could not exist on the less rigid earth.

When we gaze at the moon, then, we are looking upon a cold, dead, stony world. How striking is the contrast with the romantic view we have of it. Although during a month we get to see the moon at all times of day, we associate it with night time when it is near full. As the song puts it, 'I've got the sun in the morning and the moon at night'. Night time is for romance, and so in many mythologies the silvery moon became the beguiling goddess of love.

Night is also associated with fear and darkness, with werewolves and demons, all of which again have become linked to the moon; perhaps this explains why in a few mythologies, including those of Egypt, parts of central Asia, the Vikings and the Australian Aborigines, the sun is female and the moon male. The creature or the man who behaves oddly by the light of the full moon is moonstruck, or even a lunatic, a word deriving directly from the Latin name for the moon, *luna*. A moon-calf is a congenital idiot, or originally a misshapen birth. Moon-rakers also behave oddly. This term originated in 1787 when Francis Grose described some 'Wiltshire rusticks' who saw the moon's reflection in a pond and tried to rake it out. On the other hand, the sight of the moon reflected in water has often been considered a cure for, rather than a cause of, nervous hysteria.

The varying shape of the moon linked her to fickleness and change-ability. Fifteen thousand years ago cavemen in Spain drew representations of the moon's phases on their living-room walls; we now call the caves Altamira. In astrological circles the moon signifies listlessness and indecision. For the Babylonians the moon god Sin regulated human lives. The souls of many pious American Indians journeyed to the moon to keep company with their gods, and the Gnostics saw the moon as a ship carrying souls to the sun, waxing as it gathered souls and waning as it delivered them.

The dusky markings on the moon have contributed to its mythological role. Although westerners see a face—the man in the moon—or an old woman, others see the patterns of a hare, a three-legged toad, or, in the case of some Eskimo tribes, merely charred patches, a punishment exacted by the sun because the moon dared to sneak into bed with him!

Rare events are said to occur once in a blue moon. The term originally referred to the 13th full moon in a calendar year, a circumstance which normally happens seven times in each 19 year span. Later it was used to describe the slightly commoner occurrence of the second full moon in a calendar month. Today both of these meanings have lapsed, and we tend to refer instead to a rare atmospheric phenomenon when the moon actually is tinged blue, as can sometimes occur in the smoky air of a volcanic eruption or a forest fire.

Another origin of the expression is claimed to be an American Indian belief that the semi-precious bluish moonstone was washed up on the beaches every 21 years, when the sun and moon attained particular positions in the sky.

Those with an interest in rare events will note that it is quite possible for February to have no full moons at all, but that if that happens both January and March will have two full moons. This took place in 1866 and 1934, and will next occur in 1999.

The moon has contributed still more to our vocabulary. Monday is the day sacred to the moon goddess. Selenium is the moon metal, from the Greek name *Selene*. Moonshine whisky was illicitly distilled by night. Old beliefs, totally without justification, that staring at the moon could cause blindness gave us the now rarely-used terms 'moon-blink' and 'moon-blind.' The former was regarded as a temporary manifestation of the latter.

The honesty plant is called the moonflower, and tradition states that with it any heart can be opened. The technical name, *lunaria*, also reflects an association with the moon; the plant was so named because of its large, almost circular, translucent seed pods. We also refer to lunate shapes when they resemble the crescent moon.

Finally, three centuries ago you were not mugged, but assailed by the moon-man on his nightly prowl.

Eclipses of the moon 4

*In the tyme of the eclipis the eird is betwix
the mune and the soune.*
SCOTTISH COMMENTARY,
DATED 1549

In its monthly tour of our planet, the moon follows almost the same apparent path around the sky as the sun. But not quite. Geometrical theorems require the paths to cross at two points on opposite sides of the sky, and to be most widely separated at the intermediate positions. This can most readily be visualised by drawing equators at different slants around a ball. In the case of the sun and moon, as seen from the earth, the greatest separation is about ten times their apparent diameters.

Eclipses of the sun or moon require the three bodies to be very nearly in a straight line. In a solar eclipse, the moon intervenes between earth and sun. This can occur only at new moon. When the earth occupies the middle position it blots out sunlight from reaching the moon so a lunar eclipse occurs; the moon must then be full. The sun, of course, can never take the middle position between the earth and moon.

If sun and moon followed identical paths around the sky, there would be an eclipse of the sun every new moon, and a lunar eclipse every full moon. Because of the tilt of these two paths, eclipses occur only when the sun and moon lie near one of their crossing points—the so-called nodes of the moon's orbit. If we think of this in terms of the sun, we realise that it gets to one or the other node twice a year. Eclipses can occur a month or so either side of the node. If there is an eclipse, say, in March then there will be another around September. This is the minimum number of eclipses that can occur. If things line up optimally, two or even three eclipses can occur around each node.

Unfortunately, the moon's motion around the earth is not quite that simple. The positions of the crossing points, the nodes, are continually changing. It takes 18⅔ years for the two nodes to swing completely round the sky. Thus if eclipses happen around March and September one year, they will occur some three weeks earlier next year, around

23

February and August. Because the nodes change dates, it is possible for three sets of eclipses to occur in one year, and for this reason the maximum number of eclipses can be as high as seven. The last time that seven eclipses occurred in one year was 1982, when there were four of the sun and three of the moon, a situation that will not recur until 2094. In 1917 and again in 1935 there were five solar and two lunar eclipses, but this will not happen again until 2160. The rarest of all eclipse patterns is one in which three solar and no lunar eclipses occur: that last happened in 1908 and before that in 1535.

It was noted in chapter 3 that the moon's distance from the earth, and hence its apparent size, varies. The time between closest approaches differs from the period between full moons so some full moons are bigger than others. If a large full moon happens near the nodes, then it is more likely to clip the earth's shadow than if a similar alignment of sun, earth and moon occurs when the moon is at the most distant point of its orbit.

The changing size of the moon should not be confused with a well-known optical illusion. The moon looks bigger when it is rising or setting. The illusion is caused by the fact that when near the horizon we have familiar objects such as trees and buildings to help us judge its size. The eye acts as a sort of zoom lens, focusing attention on the moon. When the moon lies high in the sky, the brain switches our eyes into wide-angle mode, in an attempt to find something else in view. We then judge the moon to be smaller.

As a further complication, the earth orbits the sun in an elliptical path. It passes closest to the sun in early January, and furthest from it in early July. The effect is small, but is sufficient to make southern hemisphere summers slightly warmer than northern, while austral winters are a little colder. It also makes the sun appear bigger in January than July, and in turn alters the details of the earth's shadow, thereby modifying lunar eclipses.

All of these effects, and many more irregularities of the moon's orbit about the earth, must be taken into consideration when astronomers predict eclipses. Today the predictions pour out of a computer, but two centuries ago the work involved in predicting the circumstances of even one eclipse was horrendous.

Let's look at the details of a lunar eclipse.

The earth's shadow always exists, stretching out into the midnight sky. We see the shadow only when the moon passes into it, during an eclipse. If the sun were a perfect point of light, the earth would have a single cylindrical shadow that spread back into space as in Figure 4.1. Because the sun is actually large, there are many of these cylinders spreading back, one from each point on the sun's surface. Figure 4.2 shows the net effect.

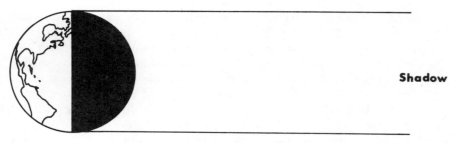

4.1 If the sun were a very distant point of light it would cast a sharp cylinder of shadow behind the earth.

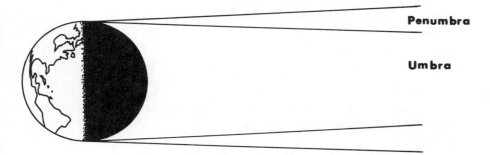

4.2 Because the sun is extended, the shadows are more complex. A converging cone, the umbra, is the resultant solid shadow, but a diverging cone called the penumbra is also formed. From within the penumbra, part of the sun is visible.

The cylinders define two shadows, called the umbra and penumbra. The umbra is the space common to all the cylinders, and is a cone which converges to a point behind the earth. The penumbra is the space within any cylinder, and it grows with increasing distance behind our planet. At any point within the umbra, the sun is completely covered by the earth. Within the penumbra, the sun is only partially covered, so the shadow is not truly dark. You can see examples of umbra and penumbra here on earth. The shadow of a very distant mountain, or even a building, has a fuzzy edge, quite markedly different from the shadow of a nearby object. The deep shade is the umbra; the fuzz is the penumbra, the part of the shadow from which some of the sun's disc can be seen.

The earth's umbra reaches back about 1.3 million kilometres, roughly three times the distance between earth and moon. At greater distances than that the earth would appear as no more than a dark, round spot covering only a part of the sun's disc, and at very great

25

distances the portion covered by the earth would be a scant hundredth of a per cent. The intensity of sunlight would be reduced by this insignificant amount, too small to measure. Other bodies, Mars and Jupiter, for instance, pass into this distant shadow zone occasionally, but we cannot register an eclipse of them because our equipment is not sensitive enough. At that time, an observer on one of those planets would see the earth move slowly across the sun's disc. Such events are called transits, and we return to them in chapter 5.

At the average distance of the moon, the umbra of the earth's shadow is about 9000km in diameter, and almost circular. It would be exactly circular but for the fact the the earth is itself slightly squashed at the poles. The moon is 3300km in diameter, and so can disappear wholly into the umbra. The moon moves its own diameter through space in almost exactly one hour. If the sun and moon are exactly at the nodes of the moon's orbit, so that the moon moves centrally through the umbra, then we will see the umbra on some part of the moon for 9000 + 3300 = 12 300km of travel, which corresponds to about 225 minutes. We will see the moon wholly within the umbra (i.e. totally eclipsed) for 9000 − 3300 = 5700km of travel, or some 105 minutes. Apart from slight changes caused by the varying distances between the three bodies, these figures represent the longest duration for a lunar eclipse.

Clearly there are portions of an eclipse when the moon is only partly within the umbra, and these are referred to as the partial phase of the eclipse. There are also occasions when the moon never passes wholly into the umbra, because it travels above or below the umbra's centre, and these are called partial eclipses. In a typical century about 150 eclipses of the moon will take place, of which 80 will be total and 70 partial.

The penumbra has a diameter of about 16 000km at the moon's distance. On either side of its passage through the umbra, the moon spends a period within the penumbra. Sometimes the moon passes through only the penumbra. This will be the case if an eclipse occurs three to four weeks away from the nodal passage. During penumbral eclipses, or during the penumbral phase of partial and total eclipses, the moon is only slightly dimmed, so that most observers are unaware of the event. The boundary of the penumbra is extremely hard to detect; it is the edge of the umbra that we see marching across the moon. In this book penumbral eclipses of the moon are ignored.

When specifying the times of an eclipse of the moon, astronomers can list a number of stages, thus:

1   Moon first enters edge of penumbra
2   Moon wholly enters penumbra

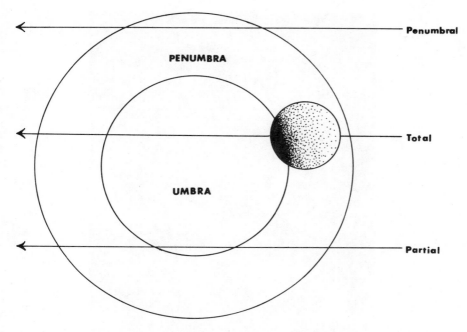

4.3 At the average distance of the moon, the earth's umbra and penumbra form this pattern. The moon is drawn to the same scale, and the lines show its path when encountering the three types of lunar eclipse.

3   Moon touches umbra; partial phase begins
4   Moon wholly enters umbra; total eclipse begins
5   Middle of·eclipse
6   Moon begins to leave umbra; totality ends
7   Moon leaves umbra; partial phase ends
8   Moon begins to leave penumbra
9   Moon leaves penumbra

It is normal in astronomical tables to give all of these times except 2 and 8, whilst newspapers and popular accounts will normally give 3, 4, 6 and 7.

The times of these stages are usually quoted for the Greenwich meridian (i.e. London) with no correction for daylight saving time. A summer eclipse in England occurs one hour later than the tables because of summer time. At other locations one must know how far ahead of or behind Greenwich the local time system is, in order to determine when the eclipse will occur. Observers to the east of the Greenwich meridian may see an eclipse on the next calendar date, in the early morning hours.

Eclipses of the moon have no respect for one's geographical location. They happen just as often in daytime as at night. Because an eclipse must occur only at full moon, when the moon is directly opposite the sun, if it happens during the day then the moon will be below the horizon. That eclipse can be seen only from the other side of the earth. Naively, then, we will see only about half of the eclipses of the moon from any point on earth. Because, in fact, most eclipses last a couple of hours, we do get to see slightly more than half of them, weather permitting, from any given spot. It is even possible, though at any one locality it is extremely rare, for the sun and the totally eclipsed moon to be above the horizon at the same time.

It was recognised a long time ago that eclipses of the moon offered a way to determine longitude by being accurate clocks visible from many parts of the earth. The difficulty of determining longitude plagued sea captains of the 17th century. Latitude they could determine by sighting the sun's elevation with a sextant, but longitude could be measured only if they had an accurate clock as well. Pendulum clocks do not run true on a pitching ship. A large sum of money was offered for any solution to the problem, which was considered one of the most fundamental limits to trade and exploration. In the end the solution came with the invention of the marine chronometer which uses a spring instead of gravity to regulate the clock.

In the interim, astronomers explored several possibilities. The exact time that the earth's shadow comes onto the moon's disc is independent of where the event is viewed from. Hence one may adjust one's clock by it, and from that adjustment determine longitude. Unfortunately, eclipses of the moon occur so rarely as to be almost useless for ships on the move. However, Christopher Columbus used this technique to fix the longitude of Jamaica in 1504, and was doubtless disappointed to find that it lay not as far west as he had hoped.

An earlier Greek attempt at the same trick compared the reported timing of the eclipse of 20 September 331 BC made at Carthage (in modern Tunisia) and Arbela in the Middle East. In this case the eclipse was not used merely to correct clocks which were to be employed for other celestial measurements. Instead, the different times read on the clocks when the eclipse began were taken to indicate the difference in longitude of the two cities. Sadly the clocks were wrong, the difference in longitude was overestimated, and maps of the region were severely distorted.

The umbra is not truly black. By rights it ought to be, since nothing brighter than starlight or distant planets shine on the moon when it is in the earth's umbra. However, this argument neglects one detail, namely the presence of an atmosphere around the earth.

We are taught at school that light travels in straight lines when in a vacuum, and so it does. But we also learn that light bends its course on entering glass or other transparent materials, so that after it has gone through a prism the direction of travel is different. The earth's atmosphere acts like a prism as Figure 4.5 shows. A ray of sunlight passing just above the earth's surface is bent round so that it actually shines into the umbra. The bend is small, and is greatly exaggerated on this diagram, but it is sufficient to illuminate the moon even when it is at the very centre of the umbra.

How much light reaches the moon by this route? That depends on the clarity of the atmosphere. Because the sunlight has to take a very long path through the air, it will be transmitted only if there is no dust or haze to block it. Eclipses of the moon are, in fact, a means of monitoring the dustiness of the atmosphere. Following a major volcanic eruption, such as that of Krakatoa in August 1883, the air is so dusty that the moon almost completely vanishes during the total eclipse, and in extreme cases it is seen only as a dark circle hiding distant stars.

The blackest eclipses in recent times were those of 4 October 1884,

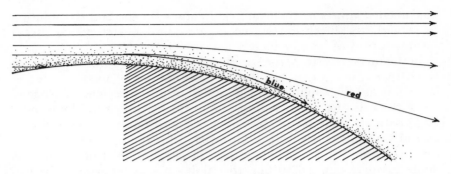

4.5 The earth's atmosphere acts as a weak prism, bending light so that it can illuminate the moon in the umbra. Although blue light is more readily bent towards the umbra, it is scattered and absorbed by dust and haze in the air, and does not emerge at all.

following Krakatoa, when observers described it as 'indian ink tint' and 'cold grey'; 22 March and 15 September 1913 following the eruption of Mt. Katmai in Alaska; and 30 December 1963 and 24 June 1964, after the eruption of Agunk volcano in Bali. The oldest record of a very dark eclipse dates to 5 May 1110, and we have no idea which volcano to blame in that case. Dark eclipses were also recorded in 1588, 1601, 1620 (twice), 1642, 1761, 1816, 1837, 1902 and 1903.

At a typical eclipse the moon may fade to one five-thousandth part of the brightness of the normal full moon. Much brighter eclipses sometimes occur, however, in which the moon seems scarcely dimmed at all; these are harder to explain. It was suggested by the French astronomer A. Danjon that the moon's surface is made to fluoresce by the radiation it receives from the sun. This idea is not widely accepted, however. Very bright eclipses were noted in 1623, 1703 and 1840, while the eclipse of 19 March 1848 changed from very bright to normal during totality, and those of 16 August 1598 and 13 October 1837 were yet more remarkable because only one part of the moon darkened, the other part remaining bright.

The dust in the air, and even the air itself, spreads blue light around and allows the red to get by. That is why the sky is blue and the setting sun red. The light that reaches the eclipsed moon is also red. When the air is clear, the moon turns a light coppery-orange during eclipse; darker eclipses are progressively deeper red. It is difficult to predict the colour in advance, and that is perhaps the most magical aspect of eclipses of the moon.

We do not have to await a lunar eclipse to see the earth's shadow, however. It is visible on any clear day just after sunset or before sunrise. Take the sunset case: as the sun sinks, the shadow of the rim of the earth on which we stand is projected out into space. First, however, it must pass through the atmosphere. If there is dust in the atmosphere, then the grains will be lit up by the sunlight and dark in the shadow. As a result, shortly after sunset there rises from the eastern horizon a shadow band in deep blue, where the high-level dust is in darkness, and above it a pinkish band, where the high-level dust is illuminated, like the eclipsed moon, by the red light of the setting sun.

This phenomenon is known as the earth shadow. It is usually best seen twenty to thirty minutes after sunset; later than that it has risen so high in the sky as to be smeared and lost to view. Mountaineers see a more spectacular earth shadow which, from their high vantage, may be visible before sunset, and which can feature a triangular shadow of the actual mountain they stand on. From very clear, high mountain sites the earth shadow is so dark that stars are seen in it; the shadow then moves across the sky, bringing stars into view eventually across the entire heavens. Perhaps this phenomenon is responsible for literary references to the curtain of night being drawn across the sky.

Lunar eclipses have left their mark in folklore and legend, often with sinister overtones. Chapter 7 will mention some of the folkloric ideas; for the present, recall the witches' brew in Macbeth, where one of the deadly ingredients was 'slips of yew silver'd with the moon's eclipse'.

5 Only in transit

*Oh most gratifying spectacle! the object of
so many earnest wishes. I perceived a new
spot of unusual magnitude, and of a
perfectly round form, that had just wholly
entered upon the left limb of the sun.*
JEREMIAH HORROCKS, 1639

In the last chapter we explained how the shadow of an astronomical object has an umbra and a penumbra, and in Figure 4.2 we showed that at great distances the umbra ceases to exist. An observer lying within the penumbral shadow zone at distances much beyond the tip of the umbra would see the earth silhouetted against the sun as a black spot. From our vantage there are two bodies that regularly do pass between us and the sun at distances such that no umbra can reach us. These are the planets Mercury and Venus, and when one or other does so we give to this extreme case of an eclipse the name transit.

Because transits are only a special form of eclipse, the conditions for the two phenomena to occur are similar. The sun, earth and planet must lie almost in a straight line, and each planet must lie near the crossing node of its path around the sky and that of the sun. Transits are a great deal rarer than eclipses, because the planets all move so slowly around the sky. Venus, for instance, lines up with the sun every 584 days, almost twenty times less frequently than the moon. The chances of this happening near a node are rare. Transits of Venus occur in pairs about 8 years apart, but those pairs can be separated by centuries. Only five have ever been observed, the most recent pair in 1874 and 1882; the next ones will be in 2004 and 2012.

Johannes Kepler, the German astronomer working in the court of Prague, was the first man to understand the motions of the planets around the sun. In 1629 he set about predicting the transits of the planets across the sun's face, a phenomenon which in those days still helped convert sceptics to the Copernican belief that the earth was not, after all, the centre of the solar system. Kepler found that transits of both Mercury and Venus would occur only a month apart in the year 1631, a circumstance that has not been repeated.

The transit of Venus occurred during the night in Europe, and passed unobserved, and Kepler calculated that the next would be in

1761. In this, however, he was wrong. A young Englishman named Jeremiah Horrocks became interested in the problem in 1638, and the following year he realised that a transit was possible in 1639. By the time he was convinced of the possibility, he had time to contact only a friend of his, named Crabtree. The two were the only living souls to see that transit, and then only in fleeting glimpses between clouds. Horrocks had a brief chance before going to church, November 24th in that year being a Sunday. He wrote in Latin to a friend the words translated at the head of this chapter.

Transits of Mercury occur roughly every 7 years, there being 14 this century. Since 1950 transits have occurred in 1953, 1957, 1960, 1970, 1973 and 1986. Only two more will be seen in the remainder of the century. That of 6 November 1993 will be visible from many inhabited parts of the world, whereas the 15 November 1999 transit may be quite unobserved. The earth barely enters the penumbra of the 1999 transit, which is expected to be visible only from Antarctica, though there is a chance that observers from the extreme southern portions of Australia will see the planet just nick the edge of the sun, never fully coming onto the disc.

Just like eclipses of the moon, half of the transits occur below an observer's horizon, unless he travels to see them. Of course, the transit must happen during the day if it is to be seen. The typical duration of a transit is 5 hours though, so that an observer who wishes to see only the beginning or end of a transit has nearly three quarters of the earth's surface to watch from, whilst an observer wanting to see the entire transit while the sun is above the horizon must position himself in the right quarter of the planet.

Mercury is a small planet, less than 5000km in diameter, and compared to the sun it is tiny. A telescope is required to see Mercury at all during its transit, and any attempt to view a transit of Mercury should be made using the projection technique described in chapter 2. Venus is both larger and nearer, so that it is just visible to the most acute human eye (safely protected by a filter) during its transit. There are no actual records of sightings of Venus in transit before 1631, and projection through a telescope or pinhole unquestionably shows it better.

Transits of Mercury and Venus are now little more than objects of curiosity, but two centuries ago they played a vital role in astronomy, thanks to the work of Edmond Halley, whose name was brought once more to our attention in 1985—86 with the passage of his famous comet. Halley argued that observations of transits could be used to yield an accurate value for the distance to the sun. This argument had actually first been propounded in 1663 by a young mathematician named James Gregory.

33

The measurement of the scale of the solar system, the diameters of planets and their satellites, the distance of nearby stars, ultimately the dimensions of the whole universe—all these depend on a knowledge of the distance between the earth and the sun. Today we have measured this with extreme accuracy using spacecraft that actually journey through the solar system. In Halley's day this was impossible, so astronomers tried to measure the position of the sun relative to distant stars from different places on the earth's surface, and so derive a distance by standard surveying techniques. The measurements had to be made to extraordinary precision. What made the job particularly hard was, of course, the difficulty of seeing stars in daylight. The observations had to span daytime, to measure the sun, and night-time, to measure the stars. The changing temperatures from day to night, caused the astronomers' instruments to warp, preventing accurate results being obtained.

Early in the eighteenth century, Halley demonstrated that transits offered a much more accurate measurement. Here was a dark spot seen against the sun itself whose position could be measured with great precision. Even simpler, by timing how long it required to traverse the sun one could calculate accurately the chord it followed across the disc. Measurements made from widely separated points on the earth would yield the required distance. The most suitable transits would be those of Venus, and would take place in 1761 and 1769; plans were duly laid to get astronomers to appropriate locations in the northern and southern hemispheres. Although extensive observations were made of the 1761 transit, from places as remote as Britain and the island of St. Helena, the results were not spectacularly good.

It was recognised that a better job could be done in 1769, but the transit had to be observed on the far side of the world from Halley's native England. In the case of the southern hemisphere this entailed sailing into relatively uncharted waters to find a stable patch of land on which to erect the instruments.

The Lords of the Admiralty mounted an expedition to sail to the recently-found Pacific island of Tahiti. The man entrusted to get the astronomers to a suitable place at the right time was a sea captain with a knowledge of astronomy and a strong will to explore new territory, James Cook.

This was Cook's first voyage into the Pacific. He took with him an astronomer named Green who has left little mark on history, and a scientist of independent means named Joseph Banks, a man who was destined to gain considerable fame in scientific circles as a result of his

5.1 a & b   This page of Captain Cook's diary records his observations of the transit of Venus observed from Tahiti in 1769.

a

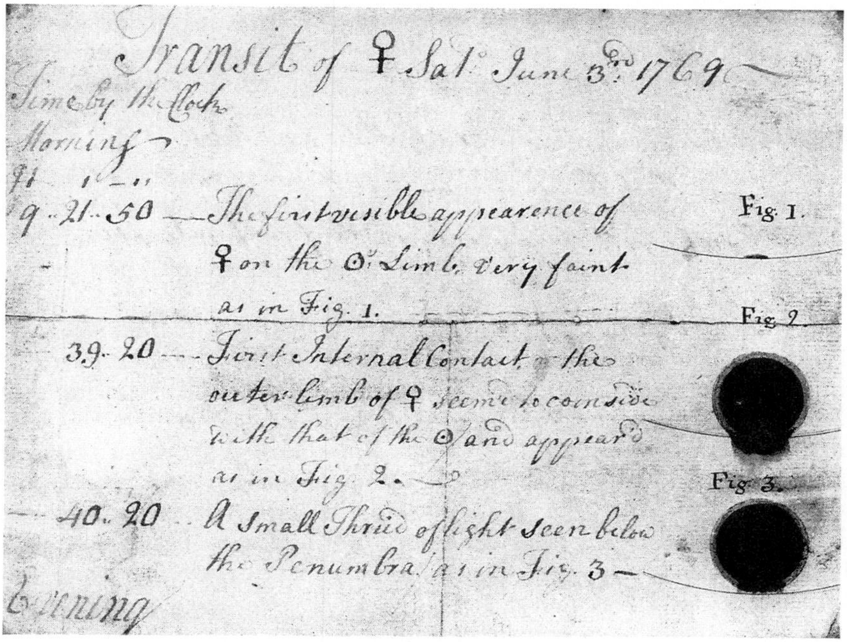

Transit of ♀ Sat.ʳ June 3ᵈ 1769

Time by the Clock
Morning

9ᵗ ¹⁻¹¹

9. 21. 50 —— The first visible appearence of
♀ on the ☉ˢ Limb, very faint
as in Fig. 1.

Fig. 1.

Fig. 2.

39. 20 —— First Internal Contact — the
outer limb of ♀ seeme to coinside
with that of the ☉ and appear'd
as in Fig. 2.

Fig. 3.

40. 20 —— A Small Thrid of light Seen below
the Penumbra, as in Fig. 3 —

Evening

b

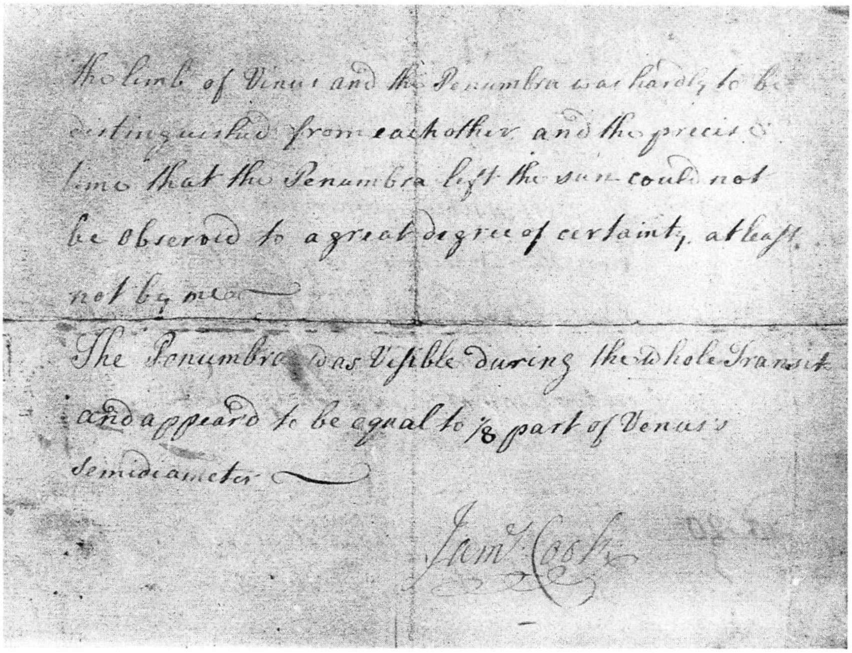

the limb of Venus and the Penumbra was hardly to be
distinguished from each other and the precise
time that the Penumbra left the sun could not
be observed to a great degree of certainty, at least
not by me —

The Penumbra was visible during the Whole Transit
and appear'd to be equal to ⅛ part of Venus's
Semidiameter —

Jam Cook

botanical and zoological work in the Pacific. It was on this journey that Cook circumnavigated New Zealand, explored the eastern seaboard of Australia, and claimed both for the King of England.

The transit was perhaps the prime motivation for Cook's expeditions in those years, but the Admiralty was also seeking the glory of acquiring for the British crown the fabled southern continent that was so ardently believed in by a few influential men. It was on Cook's second voyage that he finally laid to rest the belief in a vast southern continent to balance the land masses of Asia, Europe and North America.

For the 1769 transit of Venus, Cook navigated into Matavai Bay, Tahiti. To the east of the capital, Papeete, Venus Point can still be found on the map, one of the few geographical spots on the island that does not bear a Polynesian name. A monument has been erected, and bus loads of tourists are taken to its palm-clad lagoon as part of their guided 'exploration' of the island. Observations by Cook and Green were successful: in the final evaluation, an improved estimate of the distance from the sun was obtained, a figure that has been vastly superseded now, though in fact, it has changed by less than one per cent in later revisions.

It happened that a transit of Mercury occurred some six months later, also in 1769. Again needing a morsel of terra firma, Cook landed Green in New Zealand. The expedition had been exploring the north-eastern parts of the North Island for a few weeks by then, generally getting a pretty unwelcoming reception from the Maoris. On the Coromandel Peninsula, however, there were fewer Maoris, and they were more peaceably disposed. Mercury Bay is now a sleepy spot, off the beaten track, visited by few tourists.

It is interesting to speculate whether the British Admiralty would have mounted its Pacific expedition without the fillip of the transits. If not, Australians and New Zealanders might now be using French or Dutch as their native tongues.

Eclipses of the sun 6

High on her speculative tower
Stood science waiting for the hour
When Sol was destined to endure
That darkening of his radiant face
Which Superstition chose to chase,
Erewhile, with rights impure.
WILLIAM WORDSWORTH
The eclipse of the sun, 1820

Just as for the moon, an eclipse of the sun requires both bodies to be near a node. In this case, however, both must occupy the same node, and the moon must be new. Now, therefore, it is the moon's umbra and penumbra that are important, together with the way the earth moves through them.

Because the moon is much smaller than the earth, its umbra is also very small. In fact, the earth only just enters the tip of the umbra. This is merely a different way of saying that the sun and moon appear much the same size in the sky. When the moon is at its most distant—apogee—it appears smaller than the sun, and the umbra fails to reach the earth.

Even the moon's penumbra is smaller than the earth, so an observer on the moon, shivering in the depths of the local night, could see the entire umbra and penumbra pattern projected on the earth.

Figure 6.1 shows the three possibilities. Now it must be remembered that the events will be viewed from the object lying in the shadow, the earth. Anyone standing in the penumbra will see a partial eclipse; within the umbra, total eclipse; and within the extension beyond the umbra's cone a transit of the moon across the sun will be seen. The moon is still very nearly as big as the sun, so transit is a misleading term, and instead the eclipse is described as annular, because the tiny bit of sun still visible forms a complete but narrow ring, or annulus, around the moon.

As the sun, moon and earth move, and the earth rotates, the pattern of the shadows is swept across the earth's surface. If we ignore the slight complications produced by the earth's rotation, we can best describe the events as if we were viewing from the moon. A stage in an eclipse is shown from this perspective in Figure 6.2.

As this diagram shows, a partial eclipse is not seen from the entire hemisphere of the earth. And, obviously, no eclipse at all was seen

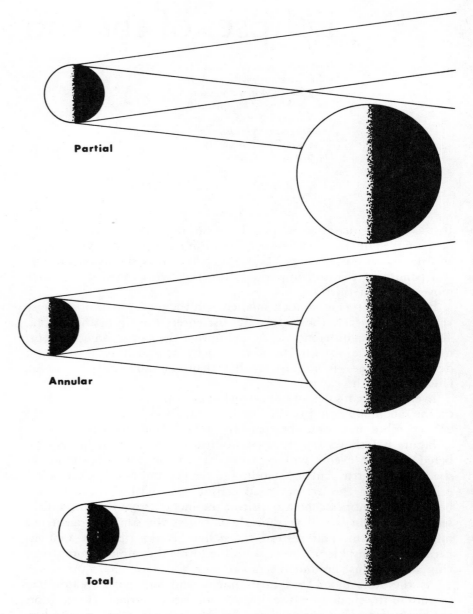

6.1   The configuration of moon and earth for the three types of solar eclipse which can occur. Not to scale.

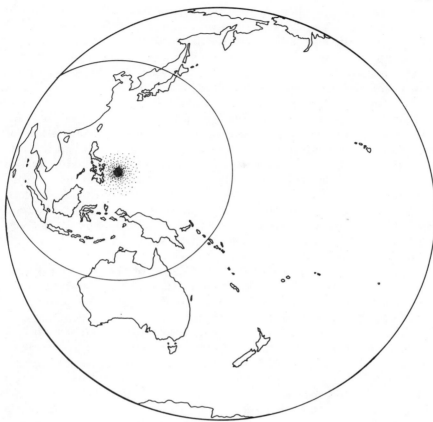

6.2   This is the view that would be had from the moon during the total solar eclipse of
18 March 1988, at 01.20 GMT. The dark central spot, the umbra of the moon, has
recently left the Philippine island of Mindanao to head into the Pacific Ocean. The softer
shadow is the penumbra, which stretches as far as the thin circle.

from the night-time hemisphere. Thus the existence of a predicted
eclipse of the sun even in local daylight is not a guarantee that an
eclipse will be seen, and this must have been a severe blow to the
astronomer-priests of ancient times who lacked the computing
facilities to do more than suggest dates on which an eclipse might
occur somewhere in the world. More important, the area swept out by
the path of the total eclipse is very small indeed; the same is true of an
annular eclipse.

There is a total eclipse of the sun most years, but rarely two in a
year. If you insist on staying put at one spot on the earth's surface
you will see a total eclipse once every four hundred years on average.

39

The northern hemisphere is favoured with a total eclipse at any one location averaging once per 320 years, compared to 640 years for the south. The difference arises because the earth does not follow a perfectly circular path around the sun. Of course, one can pick specific exceptions to these generalisations. It was, for instance, quite remarkable that from an area near Port Moresby in Papua New Guinea total eclipses were seen in both 1983 and 1984.

Now, visualise the earth as a ball as in Figure 6.2, and you will see that when the spot of the total eclipse is near the apparent edges of the planet, it is landing on a surface more distant than when it lands near the middle. The difference in the distance is the radius of the earth, 6000km, and this can be enough for the eclipse to switch from annular to total and back again. One such recent eclipse took place on 29 March 1987, and on this occasion a total eclipse could be seen for only one brief second from a very small area of the planet. In some rare cases, an annular eclipse can even be seen as total from a high mountain in its path.

In the average century about 240 eclipses of the sun take place, and of these no more than a dozen combine total and annular phases. Of the remainder, typically 70 will be total and 80 annular, and the remaining 80 or so will be only partial.

The most favourable total eclipses, those with the largest umbral shadow, occur when the moon is at perigee, its closest approach to earth. The 1973 eclipse in North Africa approached quite closely the ideal. It took place in June when the sun was nearly overhead the Sahara desert and the moon very near perigee. Under these conditions the umbral spot can be as large as 300km across, bringing totality to proportionately more of the earth's surface. It also takes longer to pass a given spot, so that the total phase of the eclipse can approach 8 minutes in duration. This is preceded and followed by rather more than one hour of partial phase.

There is considerable interest in viewing total eclipses of the sun, so predictions of their paths are made with great precision. Detailed maps are produced in which the exact boundaries of the path of totality are plotted, usually to the nearest ten or twenty metres, together with the times of the start and end of totality. The duration of the total phase is greatest at the midline of its path and falls to nothing at its edges. It is also longest near the midpoint of its route and less towards the ends. Unless the eclipse becomes annular, the ends of its route are the places where the sun rises, or sets, in the middle of the eclipse, or where the shadow drops off the earth near one of its poles. One disadvantage of these end points of the eclipse line is therefore that the sun is very low in the sky, and is more likely to be hidden by cloud as well as being dimmed by haze and dust in the air. Interest therefore concentrates on sections of the path near its midpoint, that also occur on accessible land masses.

Booklets are produced by numerous observatories, governments and amateur astronomical groups, booklets which detail not only the eclipse itself but what weather conditions are likely to prevail at that time of day and year along the path of totality. They usually also advise on ease of access and other travellers' tips, and conclude by recommending a few good locations for eclipse viewing.

There is now a fairly regular clientele of eclipse observers. Many travel to the appointed spot from halfway round the world. American and Japanese are usually the most numerous. You can watch them arriving in their hundreds, a day or two before the eclipse is due. Some will have carted with them crates of equipment—cameras, telescopes etc. Many are veterans of a dozen or more total eclipses. These are not the professional astronomers, who may have arrived a week before with considerably more sophisticated equipment; no, these are amateurs travelling for the the pure joy of seeing a total eclipse.

Over the last decade or two, it has become fashionable to take passenger liners to the sites of total eclipses. Here is an attractive alternative to the often tiresome journey to remote corners of foreign lands. The cruise may last a week or two, will have at least one professional astronomer on board, and will have a certain freedom to avoid cloud banks along the eclipse track.

What brings these folk to the eclipse track? Why do they congregate on the path of totality rather than being content with a view of the partial phase? What drives them to such major expense every year or two, just to see two or three minutes during which the sun is blacked out?

The simple answer to these questions is that only during a total eclipse can one see the flame-like prominences and pearly corona that were described in chapter 2. This is certainly the motive that has encouraged professional astronomers to undertake eclipse expeditions for upwards of 100 years. It might be regarded as a reason why amateur astronomers make one eclipse trip in their lifetime. The fact that neither prominences nor corona look the same on two successive trips may even justify more than one such trip per lifetime.

However, to understand why people—not necessarily astronomers—can get hooked on total eclipses of the sun one must go to see one, for it is an experience that defies description. We attempt a description in chapter 11, though we know that our words are inadequate. For a total eclipse of the sun is an emotional as well as a visual experience.

In ancient times, even when eclipses of the sun were understood, many people felt terror at their occurrence. The Romans, for instance, would never hold a public assembly during one. The Roman writer

41

6.3   The spread of brightness in the corona cannot be recorded photographically without special techniques. For this photograph, taken in 1973, a filter was used which transmitted progressively less light towards its centre.

Plutarch tried to dismiss these fears as superstition, but his words had little effect. Similarly the Navajo Indians of Arizona would not hold meetings during an eclipse, but would sit in silence or chanting the rites of blessing until it ended. Those of Christian faith have seen in the corona the sign of a halo, as around the Madonna's head. Peruvian peasants have been observed to fall to their knees during totality and utter the words 'La Gloria'.

Before witnessing a total eclipse, have a look at a partial one. Any of the techniques described in chapter 2 for observing the sun are fine for the job. If the eclipse covers a substantial fraction of the sun, you can monitor the temperature change, to show how dramatically we do rely on the sun's heat. Also, look at the shadow patterns beneath a tree. The gaps between the leaves act as pinhole cameras, each projecting a somewhat fuzzy crescent sun onto the ground to make an overlapping series of bright patches all of which swirl in the same way, like a futuristic painting. It can also be quite interesting to plot the course of the moon across the sun from its first to its last contact. You may find

6.4 During a partial eclipse of the sun, shadows through a tree become curved. Each small gap in the foliage acts as a pinhole, projecting a fuzzy image of the crescent sun.

that it doesn't move quite in the direction you expected; this is because of the added effect of the earth's rotation.

Try to study a partial eclipse first, because once you have seen a total one you will have no further interest in the partial kind. In writing this book the authors hope that you will be stimulated to make the pilgrimage to see a total eclipse of the sun. It is an event that will make your lives richer and more complete.

7 Astronomy and folklore

Varda commanded the Moon to journey in like manner, and passing under the Earth to arise in the east, but only after the Sun had descended from heaven. But Tilion went with uncertain pace, as yet he goes, and was still drawn towards Arien, as he shall ever be; so that often both may be seen above Earth together, or at times it will chance that he comes so nigh that his shadow cuts off her brightness and there is darkness amid the day.

J R R TOLKIEN, *The Silmarillion*

To our forebears the sun and moon were magical creatures, bodies of inexplicable nature that somehow journeyed across the sky above our heads, without falling off, and then burrowed their way through some underground route to rise once more in the east. While the sun could be likened to a fire, giving off heat and light, the moon was utterly mysterious, changing shape day by day and traversing the heavens at a different rate from its companion. Inevitably, being mysterious, they were deified, for in ancient worlds a god was synonymous with anything that could not be understood.

In most mythologies the sun was the more powerful god, the centre of attraction signifying light, life and vitality, wisdom and authority. The sun was the giver and destroyer of life; to Mahommedans, the protector of princes and sultans; to Christians, a symbol of Christ and an emblem of the Virgin. To the Egyptians, and to many Indian tribes, the sun was the resting place of the dead, journeying daily across the sky and nightly through the underworld.

Gods, especially one so supreme as the sun, had to be worshipped. Only by suitable votive offerings could they be relied upon to maintain their vital roles. In some parts of the world, the South American civilizations being prime examples, the offerings were human, and the sacrifices grisly. In other places they amounted to simple communion. Sun dances were widespread around the world as a ritual thanksgiving to the deity. In some cultures, for instance the Pawnee Indians, they were accompanied by self mutilation as a means of atonement.

Prayers and offerings to sun and moon usually succeeded: the sun continued to shine, bringing warmth, light and strength to the crops; the moon threaded its gentle way between night and day, stirring the ocean tides and maintaining the supplies of seafoods to coastal dwellers.

Sometimes, however, things went wrong. Sometimes one or other of these bodies would be eaten into by an invisible dark creature. To simple peasants who knew nothing of the workings of the sky, eclipses were fearsome events. Not only were they strange tamperings with otherwise reliable gods, but they threatened also to remove the deities for ever from the skies. Fear was as natural a reaction to an eclipse as to any other powerful event that could not be fathomed, for instance an earthquake or a fatal epidemic. The penultimate section of the Mahommedan holy book, the Qur'an, contains an incantation to ward off the evil of an eclipse.

'The moon was covered with a horrid shield' says the Anglo Saxon Chronicle of the eclipse of 23 January 753 AD, and more than 1400 years earlier the Assyrian leader Assurbanipal offered the following prayer: 'I make petition unto thee and I ascribe praise unto thee because the evil which follows the eclipse of the moon, and the hostility of the powers of heaven and evil portends are in my palace and in my land'. Of the eclipse of 1544 the monk Leovitius claimed it presaged famine, pestilence and wars with Germany.

More recently a traveller in South Africa in 1874, at the time of an eclipse of the sun, reported that 'the natives were much afraid, and went to their huts', and a record from France dated 1654 reports many people shutting themselves in cellars for the same reason. We are left to speculate whether these were wine cellars.

A story, probably much exaggerated, has Louis the Pious dying of fright at an eclipse of 840 AD. That Louis died is irrefutable, for three years later the empire that he had inherited from his father Charlemagne had to be divided among his three sons. At the Treaty of Verdun the three agreed to take France, Germany and Italy respectively.

What could possibly be attacking the sun or moon during an eclipse? Lacking the knowledge that the moon was illuminated by the sun, and that the Earth was a round object that might cast a shadow, no explanation was possible. It might be felt that explanations lay within the reasoning powers of the ancients, but it is unclear whether many did fathom out the phenomenon. We know that the Greeks did so, but their understanding was not widely disseminated. Writing of a partial eclipse of the moon in 1044 the Frenchman Raoul Glaber mused 'In what matter it happened, whether a prodigy brought to pass by the Deity or by the intervention of some heavenly body remain

7.1 The sun was of supreme importance in the mythology of ancient Egypt. This obelisk, which was erected in the time of the female Pharoah Hatshepsut, was a symbol of the sun. Its uppermost pyramid was clad in beaten gold to catch the first rays of the rising sun.

45

known to the author of knowledge. For the moon herself became like dark blood, only getting clear of it a little before dawn'.

Lacking an understanding of the event, therefore, most peoples of the world reckoned that some invisible creature was devouring their deity, its black jaws or claws ripping ever larger portions from the disc. In Iran, Lappland and the Orient the unseen creature was a dragon, and in India two dragons were required, Rahu and Ketu, according to which of the two nodes of the moon's orbit was involved. During the Middle Ages in Britain the dragon concept also took hold. Some reports of eclipses are accompanied by sightings of dragons, and eclipses at the two nodes were referred to as the dragon's head or tail as appropriate. In the Americas dragons were not popular: more familiar creatures served the purpose—coyotes, serpents or pumas for instance. Black griffins were favoured in the East Indies and wolves in Germanic lands, while the Mayans invented a monster which plunged head down towards the earth during eclipses.

Some variants on this theme are found. In Tonga, clouds alone were invoked to account for lunar eclipses. An illness of the eclipsed body was the interpretation given by Kalahari bushmen, by the Ainu of Japan and by some north American tribes. The Tlingits of Canada would actually stand together and blow towards the sun or moon to dispel the ailment. Some Canadian Indians and Eskimos preferred to believe that the sun and moon gods had moved out of place to see better what might have been going awry on earth. Other north American tribes had a less threatening mother–with–child interpretation.

Despite the scientific traditions of ancient Greece, the man in the street was likely to tell you that magicians were responsible for lunar eclipses, and that they made the moon descend from the sky to deposit some vile froth on the plants. Until quite recently, many Japanese would cover their wells during an eclipse to prevent poison falling in, and many Eskimo women turned their pots upside down for the same reason. Some African tribes thought eclipses were battles between their deities, as did the Mexicans, and among Australian Aborigines and inhabitants of the Society Islands solar eclipses occurred when the sun and moon made love. Perhaps this last idea evolved to give yet another excuse for the islanders to do the same.

The ravenous creature that could devour an entire sun or moon had to be diverted from its task. Usually this was accomplished by a mix of prayer, dance and song. The Incas lit firecrackers and whipped their dogs to make more noise, and probably ripped a few pounding hearts from the breasts of captured warriors or white-robed virgins as a further measure. The Chinese drove away their dragons by beating gongs and drums to the tune of one of their boisterous dances. In

7.2 The mudbrick building under the protective roof is Casa Grande, the remains of an observatory built by Indians of Arizona nearly one thousand years ago. Through the openings of its uppermost storey they monitored the celestial wanderings of the sun and moon.

India many would submerge themselves to the necks in their sacred rivers, while in wild west Dakota, Indians fired rifles at the moon. In countries where the celestial creatures were not frightened by noise, fires were lit or jewels hung from trees to encourage a return of the light. Tribesmen in some countries would loose burning arrows towards a solar eclipse to rekindle the sun god.

John Fryer, travelling in Iran in 1677 referred to an 'Eclypse of the Sun' on 19 August. Although no eclipse took place on that date, his description is probably reliable of the 'lamentable plight all the Mahometans were in, they supposing that Orb to be in Labour, and therefore by Prayers and Incantations concerned at its delivery, all the time beating Pots of Brass, making a noise as dreadful as the Day of Doom'. A visitor to Egypt at the time of total eclipse of the moon in 1888 watched the populace beating tomtoms and chanting prayers for two hours, and was told 'Moon go wrong; want Lord to make moon go straight. If moon go wrong, we not know when sow corn, when say prayers'.

These measures always proved successful, just as the priests foretold: in every case the sun or moon was restored to full light either before it set or by the time it next rose. The priests were duly patted on their backs and given handsome rewards of food and valuables, whilst increasing their status in the eyes of the peasants.

The priests were educated men with a thirst for power and status. What better way to gain it than to learn how to predict the coming of eclipses? Without doubt much attention was paid to the possibility of eclipse prediction. The task was not easy, for it required a very precise knowledge of the complicated motions of the moon. Even the sun is not perfectly regular in its peregrinations, moving faster round the sky in December and January than it does six months later. Finally, the apparent sizes of the sun and moon change, so that for a range of separations slightly more than one degree they can either produce a

47

small partial eclipse or no eclipse at all. By and large, however, small partial eclipses of either body passed unnoticed. It was the large partial and total eclipses whose occurrence needed to be predicted, and that was somewhat more straightforward.

A prediction of the position in the sky of the sun or moon, or indeed of any other moving object, is called an *ephemeris*, a word derived from the ancient Greek expression 'for a day' (compare with the word ephemeral, derived from the same root). By the study of cuneiform tablets, science historians have concluded that the first people who certainly could produce an ephemeris good enough to predict eclipses were the Babylonians, around 250 BC. This was uniquely possible for the Babylonians because they alone had developed the fundamentals of modern mathematics, so essential to all scientific endeavour. Their scentific prowess can be dated back a further 1800 years to the reign of Nammu who brought many regions under the control of his own city, Ur, and created a cultural renaissance under which mathematics and astronomy could blossom.

The Babylonian interest in the sky originated as a belief in the influence of the heavens on the lives of mortals. In 1500 BC, for instance, they believed that an eclipse occurring in the month of April would portend the murder of a king by his son. April eclipses occur roughly every nine years, which suggests that Babylonian monarchs of that time did not long enjoy the fruits of their rank. We might also infer that they fathered children at an extraordinarily early age. When, later, the Babylonians recognised the rhythmic patterns of eclipses, they also realised that the very ability to predict an eclipse implied that it could have no astrological significance.

Until their understanding grew, peoples of the fertile crescent had a delightfully simple explanation for lunar eclipses, namely that the far side of the moon was darker than the face directed at earth, and that when displeased the moon merely turned round. This view actually persisted five centuries later in some Greek quarters. The Bella Coola Indians of western Canada thought instead that the moon painted her face black as temporary protection against certain celestial dangers.

The English astronomical historian Richard Stephenson has analysed hundreds of cuneiform tablets held in the British Museum and elsewhere. Many of these are the astronomers' own diaries, and although many tablets are damaged or missing, there are some very complete records especially from the 5th and 6th centuries BC, at which time they were kept within an accuracy of about 5 minutes. Early Babylonian attempts at eclipse prediction can be recognised in the tablets. One astronomer, Nabu-Rimanni, wrote to his king Darius I that he and others had kept watch to see whether eclipses of the sun and moon did occur as expected, and to confirm that indeed they did.

To be able to predict eclipses it is also necessary to understand what causes them. That understanding was not widespread even by the time of Christ. To begin with, one has to recognise that eclipses of the sun occur only at new moon and those of the moon only when it is full. Again we find the oldest certain evidence of this knowledge with the Babylonians, about 750 BC. This, incidentally predates the oldest eclipse record we have found on Babylonian tablets. Alfred Noyes put it nicely:

> *In Babylon, in Babylon,*
> *   They baked their tablets of the clay;*
> *And, year by year inscribed thereon*
> *   The dark eclipses of their day;*
> *They saw the moving finger write*
> *   Its Mene, Mene on their sun,*
> *A mightier shadow cloaks their light,*
> *   And day is day in Babylon.*

Possibly independently, the Greeks gained some understanding of the phenomenon about 300 years later. Anaxagoras was the first Greek to write down an explanation, around 460 BC. Parmenides, a student of Pythagoras, argued that the earth was a ball, and Aristotle eventually realised that lunar eclipses proved this fact because the earth's shadow was round. Nearly 2000 years later Christopher Columbus quoted Greek arguments when justifying his attempt to sail westwards to the Indies. Despite this understanding however, many Greek scientists believed that an additional body, a dark object called the Antichthon, was needed to account for all the eclipses the moon underwent. The Armenians believed in a similar body. Some west African tribes came closer to an understanding, believing that the shadow of the sun pursued the moon around the sky.

The Chinese have a tradition of astronomical observation, and indeed they recorded eclipses from before 2000 BC. However, they do not appear to have made great inroads into eclipse prediction. What rudimentary ability they did develop was later lost and had to be relearnt two millenia later from missionaries. A catalogue dated around 200 BC lists two cases of pairs of solar eclipses exactly one lunation apart. There cannot be two solar eclipses at successive new moons. In each case an eclipse did indeed occur on the first new moon, and we must assume that the court astronomers erroneously thought that another eclipse might occur at the next new moon, wrote the date down, and forgot to delete it later.

We can be fairly confident that scientists of the Arab world could predict eclipses, for it was they who adopted and expanded the scientific traditions of the Greeks, eventually reintroducing them to

49

Europe. It is casually reported that in the war between the Byzantine emperor Alexius I and the Patzinaks, Alexius used the ruse of prophesying the eclipse of 21 May 1091 as a means of frightening his enemy. On the other hand, a Turkish envoy visiting London in 1724 was unaware that eclipses could be predicted at all, and thought the local inhabitants quite affected to be proclaiming the forthcoming event. When, later, they were proved right almost to the minute, he stated that they must have learnt of the event from the devil, since 'God would never correspond with such a wretched set of unbelievers as the English astronomers'.

It seems likely that Indian priests learnt how to predict eclipses from the Arabs. The Tamils and Hindus continued to refine their work so that by the 19th century they could compute the circumstances of an eclipse to within a few minutes, using a process known as Surya Sidd'hanta. The second word should not be confused with Siddharta, which was the name given to the prince who became in later life a meditator and teacher, and whom we now call Buddha.

The calculation apparently required fifteen days of work, so a 'quick and dirty' prediction, good to half an hour or so, was usually deemed adequate. In a policy of taking what little was good from the British, some Pundits opted to copy the information straight from the Nautical Almanac, so that they had only to correct from Greenwich to the local time zone. Accurate prediction had political ramifications in those days. Hindus, like the neighbouring Tamils of Sri Lanka and

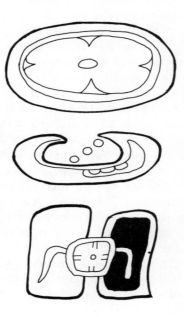

7.3 Mayan writing used pictorial symbols called glyphs. From top to bottom these are the glyphs for the sun, the moon, and a solar eclipse.

southern India, would give alms and fast for 12 hours before a solar eclipse and for 9 hours before a lunar one, and wanted a day off work for their ceremonial bathing and prayers. The Indian Government allowed a public holiday if the eclipse occurred between 6 am and 6 pm.

In 1868 King Mongkut of Thailand predicted that the eclipse which passed over his country would be total. It is not known whether he computed the circumstances himself or merely relied on European calculations, but it is interesting to note that his Royal Astronomers believed it would be only partial there.

Elsewhere in the world the only certain ability to predict eclipses resided with the Mayans, who had an ephemeris for the moon so accurate that three centuries would have to elapse before it erred by one day. The Dresden codex contains a catalogue of eclipse predictions that is reasonably reliable. Considering the dissemination of knowledge throughout Europe and Asia, it may be that the Mayans were the only people to discover the mechanics of eclipses in the last 2000 years.

Given the difficulty of the task, and that the earliest recorded predictions date from only a few centuries BC, what are we to make of the claim that as early as 2000 BC the supposedly uncultured British were able to predict eclipses with the help of that gigantic temple Stonehenge? The claim has been made by a number of eminent astronomers. It is given some credibility by Julius Caesar's record that the Druids of Gaul could predict eclipses, though Stonehenge actually

7.4 The ancient British monument of Stonehenge may have been used to predict eclipses.

predates Druidism in Britain by a very long time, notwithstanding modern claims to the contrary.

We can be quite certain that Stonehenge had some astronomical significance. The entire structure has a natural axis which points directly at sunrise on midsummer's day. It is also true that one may define sight lines between the upright stones of the monument which mark the rising or setting points of the sun and moon at various extremes of their excursions around the horizon. Whether these sight lines were deliberately set up, or have been found because so many possible lines were fed into a computer, is something that cannot be known with certainly. Statistics, for what they are worth in a case like this, suggest that the alignments were deliberate, and if we accept that view we can be confident that Stonehenge was used at least as an observatory of the sun and moon.

Around the perimeter of Stonehenge a series of pits has been found. Known as the Aubrey holes, each was dug a few feet deep and then promptly filled in with chalk rubble, so that it would have been a conspicuous white patch in the grassland. No stones or posts appear ever to have been placed in the Aubrey holes, so their purpose is puzzling. So far, only one explanation has been given for their significance. The moon's motion around the sky includes a wobble with a period of 18.6 years. This is the time taken for the two nodes of its orbit to circle the sky. To good accuracy this number can be represented by the ratio 56:3. It is therefore possible to monitor this wobble by placing three stones on the Aubrey holes, 18, 19 and 19 holes apart, and by moving each stone round one position every year.

With the help of a few other marker stones moving differently it would be possible to predict eclipses with tolerable reliability. Eclipses would occur when certain stones moved into certain positions; few eclipses would be missed by this crude technique, but some would be predicted which were invisible from Britain. The full details of this scheme were worked out by British astrophysicist Sir Fred Hoyle, who firmly believes that Stonehenge was used for this purpose. Sceptics note that merely because Sir Fred Hoyle can now use Stonehenge to predict eclipses we should not conclude that anyone ever actually did so; and moreover that this is a mighty costly way of making a device that could be handled on a piece of parchment.

Since we cannot get into the minds of the ancient Britons, the question must remain forever open. It is worth realising, however, that if Hoyle and his followers are right, then the British must have been indulging in astronomical observations for something like one thousand years before the construction of Stonehenge (about 1800 BC) in order to discover and design the mechanism. British chauvinism is clearly flattered by the suggestion that these folk were amongst the first sophisticated astronomers.

There is one extremely simple way of predicting some eclipses, a method which for its discovery also relies on some hundreds of years of observations, and on accurate record-keeping using a calendar. The method appears to have been found in a number of countries at various times, and is today known by the Babylonian name Saros. The term was adopted by Edmond Halley, though he did so erroneously, for the word refers to a particular system of measuring quite unrelated to eclipses.

If an eclipse occurs on some particular occasion, then another eclipse will occur 18 years 10 days and about 8 hours later. The reason for this is that the various periods of the sun and moon's motion all beat together at that frequency. The Saros period contains exactly 223 lunations, for instance, and therefore repeats at the same phase of the moon. Not only must the moon be at the same phase, new for a solar and full for a lunar eclipse, but it must also be at a node. The draconic month is the period required for the moon to move from one node round to the same node, and is a shorter period than the conventional month, so that 242 draconic months fit into the Saros. Note that the term 'draconic' reflects the old belief in dragons eating the sun or moon. Finally, the sun must get to a node, and in one Saros cycle it does so 19 times, to within a few hours.

When all this is put together we see that if the sun and moon were lined up at one of the nodes so as to produce an eclipse on a given occasion, they would again be pretty well lined up one Saros cycle later. The pattern of eclipses lasts for many successive Saros cycles, gradually shifting either northwards or southwards, according to which node is represented. This is best illustrated by plotting the tracks of total solar eclipses on a map of the earth. The first in the series starts near one pole, and subsequent eclipse tracks progress onto the planet and past the equatorial regions until eventually they fall off the other pole.

Because of the odd 8 hours in the Saros cycle, successive eclipses step around the earth by roughly one third of its circumference. Every three Saros cycles an eclipse will repeat almost exactly in place and in time. Try thinking back to the very first eclipse you can recall; then look out for the one which will follow 54 years and 31 days later. This is exactly how the first eclipse predictions probably began. It is, incidentally, sheer coincidence that the Saros cycle of 18 years 10 days is rather close to the moon's wobble period of 18 years 223 days, which might have been represented by the Aubrey holes.

It isn't necessary to wait for three Saros cycles to predict an eclipse: one cycle will suffice. Generally a single cycle throws the next eclipse out of view, but if, say, you saw an eclipse of the moon that took place in the early evening, then the next in the Saros cycle would, from the same location, be seen shortly before dawn.

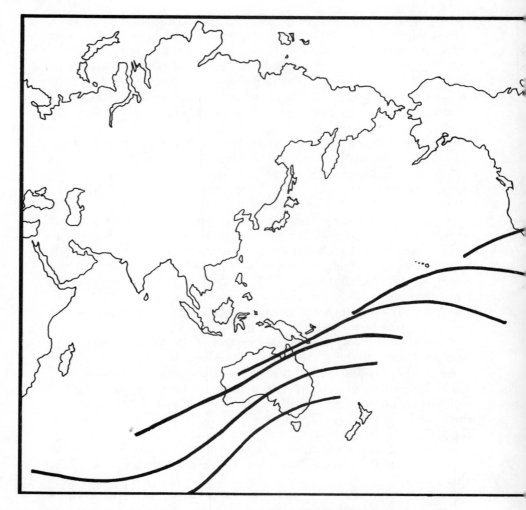

7.5   The solar eclipse tracks marked on this map are all part of a Saros cycle that began about 1000 years ago with a series of partial eclipses over Antarctica. For clarity, the path of every third eclipse is shown; the intermediate eclipse tracks form two similar interleaved patterns 120° to west and east. All the tracks shown here are annular events until the last, in 2500, which is briefly total. Thereafter several partial eclipses over the Arctic complete this Saros.

At any given time there are about 40 Saros cycles operating, and new ones start periodically to replace others that have ended. By observing every eclipse visible at a certain location over a 54 year period it is possible to predict all for the next few centuries except one or two that mark the advent of new Saros cycles. To discover that this

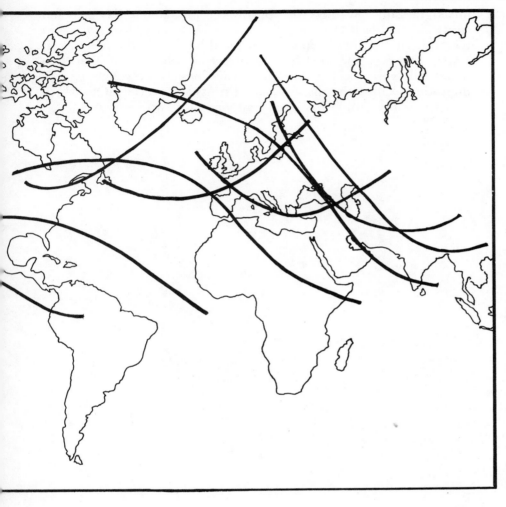

is the case, however, requires a great number of Saros cycles, especially if one has no hint of the length of cycle to begin with, nor even of its existence. A few cloudy eclipses throw out one's reckoning; moreover for the era in which the cycle was found, 54 years exceeded the adult life span of virtually everybody. How much more amazing it must be if the builders of Stonehenge found a more reliable method of predicting all eclipses.

Just occasionally, it seems, the ability to predict eclipses can be a mixed blessing. Witness the broadsheet put around London and entitled 'The Black Day, or a Prospect of Doomsday, Exemplified in the great and terrible Eclipse, Which will happen on the 22nd April 1715'. Or, pity the French country parson who in 1560, was so inundated with people seeking confessions on account of the impending eclipse that he was moved to issue a proclamation which stated that the eclipse had been postponed for two weeks.

Plate 1   Parisians watch the 1724 total solar eclipse with a mixture of fear and fascination. This painting by an unknown artist is displayed at the Observatoire de Paris.

Plate 2   In 1991 a total solar eclipse will be seen from Mauna Kea Observatory, the world's largest collection of astronomical telescopes. This, the UK Infrared Telescope, is presently the largest telescope on the 4200-metre volcanic cone. Note the shadow of the mountain beyond.

Plate 3　This photograph by Ron Royer of California shows the typical colours of a total eclipse of the moon.

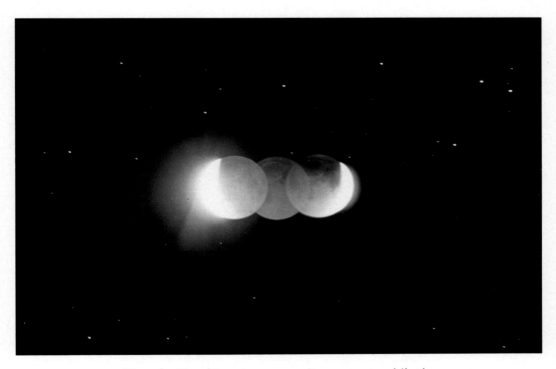

Plate 4 By taking three successive exposures while the camera tracked the background star field, Ron Royer demonstrated how the moon moves through the earth's shadow during an eclipse.

Plate 5   This photograph captures the general appearance of a
total eclipse as seen by the unaided eye. The bright point of
light is the planet Venus.

Ancient eclipse records   8

The sun and moon met in the upper sphere,
The day sin-maou, the tenth month of the
    year;
The moon was new, as she should
    reappear,
And then the sun eclipsed showed evils
    near.
The moon eclipsed before and now the sun!
Alas! We men below shall be undone.

These bodies erring, what is bad made
    known,
Good men neglected, order all o'erthrown;
The moon eclipsed was what full oft takes
    place,
The sun's eclipse portends a sadder case.
TRANSLATION BY PROFESSOR LEGGE
OF A CHINESE ODE BY A DISCIPLE OF
CONFUCIUS DESCRIBING THE
ECLIPSES OF 21 AUGUST AND
6 SEPTEMBER 776 BC

Eclipses disturb the smooth running of the heavens in a most dramatic way. It is therefore not surprising that we find frequent mention of them in the annals of many countries. Some of these references are tinged with fear, but also many are reported with nonchalance, so it would be a mistake to assume that eclipses were universally dreaded.

Ancient reports of eclipses are potentially valuable in two ways. Often the historical record can be precisely dated by the eclipse, provided that we can identify which eclipse was actually seen. Conversely, if the date has been accurately recorded, the astronomical predictions can be verified. In most cases neither is possible.

There are several problems. Firstly, the dates of many older historical events are uncertain by several years. Secondly, even if a date is given, it is not uncommon for it to be erroneous. Thirdly, some of the earlier writers did not make it clear whether they really meant an eclipse or some other phenomenon. Darkness in the daytime could refer to a total eclipse of the sun or to an unusually dark mass of cloud. Finally, the astronomical predictions are themselves uncertain.

This last matter may surprise the reader. Today we can predict eclipses to the second. Since the sun and moon move regularly round our skies, why can we not do so for eclipses past, or for that matter future? The reason is quite simply that the motions are not perfectly regular. It is true that the earth circles the sun with monotonous regularity, but it is not true that the moon circles the earth with comparable precision. At present the moon is moving gradually closer to the earth, as a result of the combined gravitational pulls it feels from earth and sun. In the past, when the moon was further from us, the month was longer, so eclipses occurred at slightly different times.

A second effect is the slowing of the earth's rotation (mentioned in chapter 3) which is not regular or predictable. If we use the present length of the day and month to compute that an eclipse which occurred 2000 years ago was overhead in, say, Cairo, then we will be in error by several hours and may find that the eclipse was actually overhead in India.

Ancient eclipses thus help to pin down these two slow changes, and to that end total eclipses of the sun are the most valuable, since to see one the observer must have been within a very small area of the earth's surface.

Given the uncertainties of ancient dates, however, how do we know which ones are reliable to determine changes in length of the day and the month? Here astronomers have to rely on historians for help, but even in collaboration an astronomer and an historian cannot always be certain of the veracity of an account. In the end it boils down to the judgement of individuals, and that means disagreement.

Most of the work of identifying ancient eclipses was done around the middle of last century. One hundred and fifty years earlier Edmond Halley had first drawn attention to the fact that old records did not tally with the best calculations he could undertake. However, like so many aspects of astronomy that involve vast amounts of computation, not many people were prepared to tackle the problem until well into the 19th century, when calculating machines had been invented.

Various astronomers and historians argued at length over whether particular eclipses were or were not useful for this purpose. A great deal of paper was used up in the publication of their various claims, and a great deal of temper was expended. Yet even today there is no consensus on who was right.

About 80 years ago an astronomer–historian by the name of Fotheringham produced a list of 11 solar eclipses from 1063 BC to 364 AD which he regarded as unequivocal and accurate. Recently David Clark and Richard Stephenson listed 27 reliable eclipses from 1375 BC to 1567 AD. Not one eclipse is common to these two lists: there is total disagreement.

The present authors are not qualified as historians to express preferences for any catalogue of so-called reliable eclipses. We can, however, recount some of the descriptions and circumstances involved.

One need not long delve into the eclipse literature to note that most of the archaic eclipses are linked to wars, battles or deaths. It is easy to gain the impression that the ancient world was perpetually at war. To some degree that was true. Often a chronicle would list only two or three events for any particular year. For instance, the Anglo-Saxon Chronicle tells us that in the year 734 AD 'The moon was [as] if it had been spilled with blood, and Archbishop Tatwine and the Venerable Bede died and Eigberht was hallowed bishop'. It recounted only the most important happenings: wars and the deaths of famous men tend to be regarded as such.

Again, the Greek traveller and raconteur Herodotus recorded that a total eclipse of the sun occurred in the midst of a battle between the Lydians and the Medes, and that the event so shocked both sides that they declared a truce. Herodotus tells us that Thales predicted the eclipse, a point to which we shall return. A later Greek historian, Thucydides, claimed that throughout the Peloponnesian wars earthquakes were more violent and eclipses more common than at any other time.

It is salutary to note how common in today's news are reports of wars, battles, and the deaths of famous people. As an exercise, take from chapter 13 the date of the next eclipse. On that night, take note of the top two or three news items. It is a fair bet that one of them will be an act of terrorism, or civil war, a serious accident involving heavy loss of life, or a murder. Times have not really changed very much.

The Anglo-Saxon Chronicle mentions quite a number of eclipses of both the sun and the moon, most of them in its later years, after about 1000 AD. The earlier records include some of the very first reports of eclipses in Britain, though as we have noted, the builders of Stonehenge may have been recording eclipses three millenia earlier. Again we have to be prepared to reinterpret some of the dates in order to make sense of what was written. A simple problem in handwriting probably explains why the lunar eclipse of 802 AD was dated 13 days before the Calends of January, instead of June. There is a ten day error in the reporting of a solar eclipse that occurred on May Day 664 AD, and another solar eclipse on 16 July 807 actually occurred two years later than stated. The lunar eclipse referred to on Christmas night 827 AD occurred a year later.

A Christmas eclipse of the moon was correctly recorded early in the 9th century in the Welsh volume *Brut y Tywysogion* (*Chronicle of the Princes*) by ab Ithel: 'Eight hundred and ten was the year of Christ when the moon turned black on Christmas day'.

A few other eclipse records of interest have survived from this period. 'With his army spread far and wide throughout the country', runs a Belgian record, 'the emperor was holding the army of Calabria when behold an unexpected eclipse of the sun struck all with great fear.' The emperor was Otto I of the Holy Roman Empire, and the date was 22 December 968. The same eclipse was seen by Liudprandus, an Italian ambassador sent to Constantinople to arrange the marriage of Otto's son (later Otto II) to the daughter of the Byzantine emperor Romanus II. In lighthearted vein Liudprandus wrote 'while I was seated at the table eating crumbly bread, the sun, as if ashamed of such villainy, concealed the rays of his light'.

An earlier record also from Constantinople describes a violent thunderstorm following the eclipse of 8 August 891. George the Monk wrote that seven people were killed by lightning on the steps of the forum of St. Constantine.

The disagreements among scholars become most severe for the oldest eclipses, and few concur on whether any eclipse prior to 800 BC can be trusted. About 900 BC an eclipse of the sun occurred at Ninevah at the coronation of the Assyrian King Assurnazirpal—this was deemed a good omen; however, the dates of Assyrian monarchs are not accurately known, so the eclipse cannot be identified. The oldest Babylonian eclipse which can unquestionably be identified, and which was observed very precisely, was that of 1 May 695 BC, in the fifth year of the ruler Assurnadinsum.

In 1987 two Californian science historians realised that a record in the ancient Chinese book called *The Bamboo Annals* was a very precise record of an eclipse. Residents in the city of Zheng saw a 'double dawn' on 21 April 899 BC. This is now recognised as being caused by a total eclipse of the sun just minutes after it rose.

There is probably a reliable mention of an eclipse of the moon in a fragment of an ancient Chinese book, and this is believed to be that of 29 January 1136 BC. Being a lunar eclipse, it is not very useful in tying down the changes in the earth's rotation. Solar eclipses that have been thought reliable were 31 July 1063 BC in Babylon when 'day was turned to night, and fire in the midst of heaven', and 3 May 1375 BC in Ugarit, at 'new moon in the month of Hiyar', when it was said that 'the sun was put to shame and went down in daytime'. The 1063 eclipse is now reckoned to have been a thunderstorm.

Homer in his 'Odyssey', has Theochymenus noting that 'out of the heaven withered and gone is the Sun, and an evil mist hovers over all'. This may be a reference to the total eclipse of 16 April 1178 BC. A possible mention of an eclipse can also be found in Genesis xv 12, and some scholars have identified it with that of 13 July 1927 BC.

Earlier still we find a much-publicised reference which shows that the Chinese were active in observational astronomy four thousand years ago. Popular versions of the tale tell that Hsi and Ho were beheaded for failure to predict a particular eclipse. In fact, they were executed because they failed to organise the dancers, archers and drum-beaters normally required to drive away the dragon thought to be devouring the sun. And why did these unfortunate public servants fail? According to the Chinese annals they were too inebriated!

The following bit of doggerel has evolved and is oft repeated:

> *Here lie the bones of Ho and Hsi*
> *Whose fate though sad was visible.*
> *Their crime was failure to predict*
> *Th'eclipse which was invisible.*

Yet this version embodies a further error: at the end of the second line the original read 'risible'. Exactly why the eclipse was said to be invisible also isn't clear.

Hsi and Ho's nemesis has been dated between 2165 and 2128 BC, with 10 October 2136 thought to be the most likely. The same eclipse was probably in the mind of Noyes when he composed the following:

> *In old Cathay, in far Cathay,*
> *Before the western world began,*
> *They saw the moving font of day*
> *Eclipsed, as by a shadowy fan;*
> *They stood upon their Chinese wall,*
> *They saw his fire to ashes fade,*
> *And felt the deeper slumber fall*
> *On domes of pearl and towers of jade.*

The oldest claimed record comes from India. A book known as the Rig Veda lists eclipses from around 1300 BC, and includes one that has been suggested to be that of 20 October 3784 BC.

More recent Indian references are fairly rare. One of interest is described in a brass plate found in Bengal in 1809. The inscription records how Prince Janamajaya 'performed a sacrifice ... at the confluence of the rivers Tungabhadra and Harida, at the time of the partial eclipse of the sun which fell on a Sunday in the month of Chaitra'. The plate apparently refers to the eclipse of 3 April 889 AD, which was also reported in Constantinople.

From classical writers alone we can identify nearly twenty further eclipses of the sun before the birth of Christ, and some of these have received a great deal of attention. The eclipse mentioned earlier, at the time of the Lydian-Median wars, has particularly exercised scholars who have finally reached almost complete agreement on its date, 28 May 585 BC. The reason for selecting this one, out of several other possible eclipses between 583 and 610 BC, was the statement that Thales had predicted it. It seems very likely that Thales was familiar only with the Saros cycle, in which case he could have predicted one eclipse by knowing of a previous one, and that was possible in this case only from

61

the eclipse of 603 BC. However, an implication of this date is that Herodotus incorrectly recorded the name of the leader of the Medes. He did get right the Lydian leader, a chap called Alyattes, father to the more famous Croesus.

Another famous classical eclipse overtook Agathocles while on a six day journey through the Mediterranean. This was no luxury cruise, for Agathocles was being pursued by the Carthaginian fleet, and indeed had just escaped a blockade in the harbour of Syracuse. The eclipse occurred on 15 August 310 BC, and it has been possible to infer the route taken by Agathocles from the fact that on his second day out he happened to sail into the shadow of totality.

Less well dated is a solar eclipse that took place in either 431 or 433 BC, in the first year of the Peloponnesian war. Pericles calmed the Athenian troops by telling them that Anaxagoras had worked out why eclipses occur, that they were quite normal occurrences, and were not to be feared. In fact Anaxagoras' realisation had been inspired by the eclipse of 30 April 463 BC. The same eclipse inspired the poet Pindar who penned this paean:

> O star supreme, reft from us in the daytime! Why hast thou perplexed the power of man and the way of wisdom, by rushing forth on a darksome track? Art thou bringing on us some new and strange disaster? Is it a signal of war, or a portent of famine: does it mean a heavy fall of snow, or is the sea to overflow the land, or fields be icebound, or the south wind bring rain, or a deluge overwhelm the world and drown all men?

On the 27 August 413 BC a total eclipse of the moon occurred when the Athenians under Nicias and Demosthenes were attacking Syracuse. It does seem a remarkable coincidence that eclipses should be linked with two battles around this city. In this case, the Athenians were upset by the changing colour of the moon, delayed too long as a result, and lost.

The first Roman reference to an eclipse of the sun was given by Livy, and took place on 11 February 217 BC during the second year of Hannibal's Italian campaign. The year before, Gaulish mercenaries in the service of Attalus I, the King of Pergamum, were halted in their advance by an eclipse of the moon, which they greatly feared.

The best known Roman reference is to one which reputedly occurred when Caesar crossed the Rubicon. This was in 49 BC when Caesar led his army from his own province in the north of Italy to march on Rome. Unfortunately it is now certain that there was no eclipse then, and the originator of this misinformation, one Dion Cassius who wrote 250 years later, may have been referring to an eclipse that occurred 21 months earlier. Cassius was possibly also recalling that a total eclipse of the moon occurred just after Alexander the Great crossed the Tigris to fight Darius, on 20 September 331 BC. Alexander clearly had some inkling of what caused the eclipse, because he made sacrifices to the sun, moon and earth.

Another Roman record parallels Pericles' efforts to quell the uneasy troops: Sulpicius Gallus, a military tribune, found himself explaining what was happening to the moon, on the eve of the battle of Pydna between the Romans and the Macedonians, in 168 BC. Later, during the reign of that bloodthirsty emperor, Nero, the Romans reported many more eclipses and other celestial phenomena than usual, though they would have seen the normal number.

8.1   This Babylonian tablet, number 45745 in the British Museum collection, includes a reference to the solar eclipse of 136 BC. Reproduced courtesy of the British Museum.

According to Richard Stephenson, the most precise eclipse record from before the invention of the telescope was that of 15 April 136 BC, described thus in a clay tablet (and translated by Abraham Sachs): 'Daytime of the 29th 24 us after sunrise, a solar eclipse on the south west side when it began. Venus, Mercury and the normal stars were visible; Jupiter and Mars . . . were visible in that eclipse . . . moved from SW to NE. 35 us for obscuration and clearing up.' The Babylonian unit of time, the us, was close to four minutes in length.

Several allusions to eclipses of the sun can be found in the Bible. None of these can easily be identified. A reference in Amos (viii, 9) possibly can be dated to 763 BC, and another in Isaiah (xxxviii, 5-8) to an eclipse which occurred during the reign of Hezekiah over the Hebrews in Jerusalem. The latter was viewed by the Hebrews as a divine sign of protection against the Assyrians under Sennacherib, and indeed the Assyrian army was decimated by illness picked up in the marshes of the Nile. The best estimate for the date of this eclipse is 11 January 689 BC.

Great signs in the sky, comets and eclipses in particular, were popularly expected to usher in the Messiah, and were much in vogue amongst Jews for several centuries after the birth of Christ.

The Chinese records were quite precise about eclipses of the sun. A book known as the Chun Tsew, written by Kung Foo Tze (whom we call Confucius) or one of his disciples, lists 36 eclipses between 720 and 495 BC, of which 32 genuinely occurred. A further 56 between 481 BC and 1361 AD are given in another tome. Curiously, all of these are solar eclipses: not a single lunar eclipse merited mention. In this regard it is of interest to quote again the Chinese record of the eclipse of 776 BC that we used at the beginning of this chapter. The translation is by the same person, Professor Legge, but now follows the original Chinese verbatim. In addition to stating quite precisely that lunar eclipses were considered to be of no significance, it gives an indication of how much editing can be concealed in the translation of poetic works. This version shows why some scholars believe the

63

original author was seeking to reprimand a particularly dissolute ruler
named Yu-wang.

At the conjunction in the tenth month
On the first day of the moon, which was sin-maou,
The sun was eclipsed,
A thing of very evil omen,
Then the moon became small,
And now the sun became small,
Henceforth the lower people
Will be in a very deplorable case.

The sun and moon announce evil
Not keeping to their proper paths,
All through the kingdom there is no government,
Because the good are not employed.
For the moon to be eclipsed
Is but an ordinary matter;
Now that the sun has been eclipsed,
How bad it is!

The mediaeval view 9

On the fifth night in the month of May the moon appeared in the evening brightly shining, and afterwards by little and little its light waned so that as soon as it was night it was so completely quenched that neither light nor orb, nor anything of it, was seen. And so it continued very near until day, and then appeared full and brightly shining.
ANGLO-SAXON CHRONICLE,
1110 AD

As we move into the Middle Ages we find more reliable and valuable European references to eclipses, and other records from further afield. For the astronomer, the more precise descriptions help to pin down the moon's motion with greater accuracy, but the shorter time span from the present (less than 1000 years), reduces the accuracy with which we can measure the minute effects. Moreover, caution still cannot be abandoned: as we shall see the annals are not yet free from error.

Consider, for instance, the occasion of the battle of Stiklestad, in northern Norway. The Norwegian king Olaf, who had introduced Christianity to the country, was being troubled by Danish invaders led by the infamous Cnut (Canute), the English-Danish king whom legend records demonstrating his egotism by trying to halt the tide. With the help of a little bribery, Cnut had won over virtually all the Norwegian nobility by the year 1028. Olaf, however, raised an army and took on the invader on 29 July 1030; he was killed in battle. The sagas of the Norse kings relate that 'the heavens and the sun became red, and before the battle ended it became as dark as night'. The Norse bard Sigvad, then in Rome, wrote:

> *No common wonder in the sky*
> *Fell out that day—the sun on high,*
> *And not a cloud to see around,*
> *Shone out, nor warmed Norway's ground.*
> *The day on which fell out this flight*
> *Was marked by dismal, dusky light.*
> *This, from the east, I heard the end*
> *Of our great king it did portend.*

Historians and astronomers long battled over this eclipse, for both could independently determine the date of the event. At length it was conceded that the battle took place 33 days before an eclipse of the sun which was probably total in Stiklestad, and which was also recorded in Ireland. Apparently the saga writers of the time conveniently shifted the eclipse to fit the battle. After his death, Olaf was sanctified by the Norwegian Church, and it has been suggested that the fiddling with dates was done to draw parallels between his death and that of Christ on the cross. In like manner a claim that a solar eclipse accompanied the death of Queen Anne on 1 August 1714 must be ignored: the eclipse took place on 22 April 1715.

Some centuries later another Norwegian king was involved with an eclipse of the sun. Haco IV led an expedition against Alexander III of Scotland to lay claim to the disputed Hebridean islands. Haco put into Ronaldsvo in the Orkneys when, according to the Norse Chronicles 'a great darkness grew over the sun so that only a little ring was bright round his orb'. Most have thought this to be a description of an annular eclipse, but recent calculations suggest that Ronaldsvo lay just outside the region of annularity, so that the ring around the moon would have been incomplete. The date was 5 August 1263.

An earlier annal which may describe an annular eclipse comes from the Swiss monk Bernoldus, 23 September 1093: ' A kind of circle appeared in [the sun] and it shone very darkly in a clear sky'.

For the first unequivocal description of an annular eclipse we must wait until 1601, again in Norwegian records. Norse fishermen near Bergen saw the moon 'contained within the sun so that there did appear a bright circle round the moon'. No records have come down of an earlier annular eclipse across Britain in 1502, perhaps because of cloud. If that is the reason, then Henry Lord Clifford would have felt a little cheesed off, for he deliberately built Barden Tower, in Yorkshire, from which to view the eclipse.

Another report of an eclipse coinciding with a battle comes from Crècy, where Edward III took on a much larger French army in the first major battle of the Hundred Years war. The place was Picardy, to be remembered in a later battle, and the date was 26 August 1346. In the first effective use of massed archers and infantry against cavalry, Edward won, establishing England as a significant military power. This eclipse is easy to dismiss, however, for the moon was then at first quarter. The error probably arose when Henry VIII had the French chronicle translated, the relevant passage coming out as 'a clyps with terryble thonder'. Dense cloud was presumably the culprit.

Some centuries later, at the battle of Austerlitz, the opposite occurred: the sun shone forth suddenly shortly before Napoleon's army captured the town. Napoleon was a superstitious character, and regarded the sun's appearance as a good omen. The expression 'sun of Austerlitz', meaning unexpected good fortune, persists to this day in parts of Europe.

By the Middle Ages we tend to find the most reliable reports of eclipses to be those not associated with wars and battles, and this should perhaps cause us to question the ancient coincidences. The total eclipse which occurred over London on 20 March 1140 is a good example: it was quite factually reported. It happened 'near the noontide of the day when men were eating, and men lighted candles to eat by', a description that originates in the Anglo-Saxon Chronicles but is confirmed elsewhere. Calculations show that totality occurred about 3pm, which may cast some light (so to speak) on the eating habits of Londoners of the time. Was this the eclipse that inspired Milton?

> *O dark, dark, dark amid the blaze of noon,*
> *Irrecoverably dark, total eclipse*
> *Without all hope of day.*

Again, the total solar eclipse of 17 June 1433 crossed Scotland and was of unusually long duration. Common folk about their daily activities saw it and were perplexed; the popular reference to Black Friday, which refers to the eclipse during the crucifixion of Christ, was perhaps reinforced by this event. Black Saturday also entered popular parlance for a while from 1598, when another total eclipse painted its dark stripe across the borders of England and Scotland on 25 February; clearly this eclipse was less memorable, for Black Saturday is no longer a common figure of speech.

The Irish equivalent of these events is Mirk Monday, 8 April 1652. Dr Wyberd, observing this eclipse from Carrickfergus, had a strange view of the event: 'the moon all at once threw herself within the margin of the solar disk with such agility that she seemed to revolve like an upper millstone, affording a pleasant spectacle of rotatory motion'.

If we seek a record from the Isle of Man we must look to 1185, when it occurred 'on the day of Philip and Jacob' namely the first of May. A single eclipse record from mediaeval times can be loosely attributed to the Americas. According to the Norse sagas the explorer Lodin was overtaken by totality to the south of Greenland; it was probably cloud rather than eclipse. At the other extremity of European influence around that time, records come from the Crusaders to the Holy Land. Fulcher was a French priest from Chartres who accompanied the first Crusade and settled in Jerusalem. Three years before his death there he witnessed the total solar eclipse of 11 August

1124, noting that the sun resembled a 'new hyacinth', or a kind of 'horned eclipsed moon'.

Also from the Crusades we find mention of the 26 October 1147 eclipse when the sun hid half his face in shame following the defeat of the German Crusade army west of Ankara.

We can recognise errors in some accounts of eclipses even as late as 1688. In that year the diarist Evelyn reported that an eclipse of the sun was seen in the morning of 24 October, the birthday of James II. We now know that the eclipse was not seen from Britain, having ended before sunrise. It seems that Evelyn either took records from further east, or relied on a rather inaccurate prediction. Similarly two centuries earlier it was noted that a total eclipse accompanied the death of another Queen Anne, the consort of Richard III, the last of the Plantagenet kings of England. Well, it did occur, but in the south of Europe, and was only seen as a partial eclipse from Britain.

Eclipses of the moon attracted fewer comments in the Middle Ages. When they were seen they were noted in the diaries, but provide little insight into popular thinking at the time. One unusual record from a monastery near Salerno in Italy, notes that a bright light was seen on the moon during the total eclipse of 6 August 1096. We find other references to lights on the moon during eclipses, sufficient to cause us to ask what they might mean. There seem to be two possible explanations. If the eclipse is not too dark, one or two of the brightest craters, particularly one called Aristarchus, can appear quite prominent and give the impression of being a local spot of light. Alternatively, bright stars or planets can be seen near the moon and may look to be on its surface. When the moon passes in front of a star the event is called an occultation, though in effect it is but another special case of an eclipse. The oldest record of an occultation occurred during the eclipse of 23 November 755 and was witnessed by one Simeon of Durham. An occultation of the planet Jupiter, not during eclipse, was reported on 31 January 807.

Predictions of eclipses were commonplace by the 16th century, but were not always reliable, and this may be why some misreporting occurs. On a cloudy day or night the uninitiated would be hard put to tell whether the eclipse did occur as prophesied. We have examples of eclipse predictions working the other way, however. In 1504 the intrepid Christopher Columbus had had to put in to Jamaica because marine worms had rendered his ships unseaworthy. While some of his crew took a smaller vessel to seek help, he and about 100 of his men remained with their ships. As food supplies ran low they traded with the natives for more, but after some months the natives got bored with Spanish gifts and became stroppy.

Columbus worked out a clever ploy. His almanac showed a total eclipse of the moon on the night of 29 February; he sent a message to the natives to the effect that because they were refusing their help he would cause the moon to show its anger. The ploy worked: as the eclipse began the natives were awed, and Columbus' party was given all the food it needed until rescue came. Columbus also timed the eclipse and was able to determine the longitude of Jamaica from his measurements.

Another traveller, on friendlier terms with the locals, also carried an almanac that showed a lunar eclipse, on Good Friday 17 April 1772. The man was James Bruce, the natives were Abyssinian tribesmen, and on this occasion Bruce's warning and explanation of the event saved them from some anxiety over the dimming of the moon. These and other such events clearly indicate that an almanac giving details of forthcoming eclipses was considered essential material for all travellers and missionaries who ventured far from Europe in the Middle Ages, or even quite recently.

An almanac fell into the hands of the American Indians in 1806 at a time when the Shawnees were trying to unite all tribes to resist the slow juggernaut of paleface settlement. One clever Indian leader used its prediction of an eclipse on 16 June to demonstrate to his followers the power he wielded, much as Columbus had done three centuries earlier.

Eclipses of the 12th and 13th centuries seem to have been particularly well reported. The best were those of 19 March 1133 and 3 June 1239, both total solar eclipses. Of the former, the American astronomical historian Robert Newton found 36 independent records, from Ireland, England, Belgium, France, Germany, Austria and Czechoslovakia. To these we can add the English Channel, for the Anglo-Saxon Chronicle records 'In this year King Henry went overseas at Lammas, and the next day, when he was lying asleep on board ship, the day grew dark over all the lands, and the sun became as if it were a three-nights'-old moon, with stars about it at midday'. Calculations confirm that totality did occur near noon, which leaves, as an exercise to the reader, the question of why Henry was in bed at the time. William of Malmesbury, writing from England, noted that 'the sun covered his bright head with gloomy rust, as the poets are accustomed to say'. We do not know what to make of the report from Heilsbronn, in Germany, that 'streams of water were brought to a stop' by the eclipse.

Yet more records of the 1239 eclipse exist, and even restricting ourselves to diarists who witnessed the total phase we can list the following cities: Cerrato and Toledo in Spain, Montpellier in France, Arezzo, Cesena, Florence and Siena in Italy, and Spalato in Yugoslavia.

Through the 16th and 17th centuries European references to

eclipses become fewer in number, though the eclipses themselves remained as common as ever. Now that they could be accurately predicted, much of their magic was lost, so diarists ceased to record them.

Early in the 18th century, however, gentlemen of leisure began to view eclipses as objects of curiosity, and references to them increased once more. Consider, for example, these records from Edinburgh, where annular eclipses of the sun occurred in 1737 and 1748.

At the first, a contemporary account tells that 'gentlemen by no means short sighted declared themselves unable to discern the moon upon the sun without the aid of a smoked glass', presumably because they were dazzled by the outer ring of sunlight. Clearly several studied the event out of pure curiosity, and had planned ahead to the extent of blackening glass for safer viewing.

At the second of these events the locals' interest in the eclipse was better described: 'there was something very entertaining in the annular appearance, a phenomenon that was equally new to all who saw it, that gave great delight to the curious, without striking terror into the vulgar'.

By the 18th century too, scientists began to study eclipses. Kepler was one example. A German by birth, Kepler worked as court astronomer in Prague. He is remembered most for his brilliant analysis of the motions of planets about the sun, work that set the foundation not merely for simple and accurate means of predicting their position in the sky (and for that matter, of predicting eclipses), but also for the understanding of the force of gravity that Isaac Newton subsequently gave us. In 1620 Kepler was the first to explain why the moon turns red during a total eclipse.

On 12 May 1706 a total eclipse of the sun coursed across Europe, causing the Geneva Council to adjourn because of the darkness. The councillors left their chamber to find many of the citizens prostrate in the street offering prayers. However, the Italian scientist Cassini made careful observations of the event. He saw several prominences, and gave us the term corona to describe the bright outer atmosphere of the sun. Previous to this event, direct references to the corona are less conclusive. The Roman author Plutarch referred to light that surrounds the sun even at mid eclipse, but it is unclear whether he referred to a total or an annular event.

It was nine years later, in 1715, that the celebrated English scientist Edmond Halley set the study of eclipses of the sun on a scientific basis. On 22 April that year, the path of a total eclipse crossed southern England, passing just north of London. To Halley this event offered opportunities both to study the event and to test his predictions.

Possibly of greater interest to him was the chance to pin down, very accurately, the position of the moon. Halley was already aware that earlier eclipses did not tally with calculations based on contemporary data on the sun and moon; indeed, he had discovered the fact. To derive an accurate measurement he stationed a series of observers in a line across each edge of the predicted shadow track. He could therefore determine the edge of the shadow to a few metres, according to which of his observers saw the sun totally obscured and which experienced partial eclipses. This gave an accuracy about one hundred times better than was possible by simply observing the position of the moon relative to background stars.

At the same time, Halley stationed himself near the centre line to study the phenomenon itself. He gave a good description of the corona, and also saw the chromosphere, the hydrogen-red zone immediately above the sun's surface and from which prominences rise. In both the scientific observations he attempted and the quality of the results he obtained, Halley showed once more that he was a scientist ahead of his time. His work remained the best available for more than a century.

Another nine years were to pass before a convenient total eclipse came to Europe, this being the next in a Saros cycle which included the Geneva eclipse. Both London and Paris lay in its path, the former being under cloud and the latter clear. French astronomers gave a poor description of the event, and in Britain nothing new was learnt.

Nine years later again, the path of a total eclipse crossed Sweden, and observations were made by a large number of clergymen. Although not scientifically trained, these gentlemen left superbly detailed descriptions which were collated by Celsius, the Swedish scientist we now associate with a scale of temperature. The Swedish clergy recorded several prominences during that eclipse.

There then followed many bleak years. Total eclipses did not dispose themselves conveniently to the astronomers of the day, who were in general unable to make the lengthy journeys necessary to view them. Instead, celestial voyeurs busied themselves with other matters, and only a few travellers witnessed total solar eclipses. One such traveller was a Spanish Admiral by the name of Don Antonio Ulloa who happened to sail his ship, the *Espagne*, into the path of the eclipse of 24 June 1778. Ulloa gave a good description of the event, seeing both corona and prominences. The most travelled man of the times, Captain James Cook, failed to encounter a total solar eclipse on his epic voyages, but did make observations of two partial eclipses —one from Newfoundland (5 August 1766) and the other from Christmas Island in the middle of the Pacific Ocean (30 December 1777).

One astronomer did attempt to travel to the track of a solar eclipse.

71

He was an American named Samuel Williams, and the eclipse took place on 27 October 1780. This was a troubled time for the young nation, and Williams had some difficulty organising his expedition. When finally he did so, he sailed in the galley *Lincoln* to Penobscot Bay, Maine, only to find that the eclipse was not total there after all. It is difficult to reconstruct exactly why Williams missed the track of totality. One reason may well have been the inaccuracy of his maps, and another the comparable inaccuracy of existing tables of the moon's motion. It does seem, however, that Williams may have erred in his own calculations.

The resurgence of interest in total solar eclipses was not to occur until the middle of the 19th century. When it came, it opened up a golden age during which astronomers were not only to learn about many subtleties of our pet star, but also to test one of the most fundamental of all laws of physics.

Plate 6   A more detailed view of the corona and prominences
as recorded with a telephoto lens.

Plate 7 Before colour photography of eclipses was possible, artists were employed to produce pictures such as this, which shows the 1851 eclipse.

Plate 8   The shadow of the earth, with its ruddy rim, can be seen on any clear evening just after sunset. Here the umbra is blue because light enters from the air around us. At the distance of the moon the red rim would have filled in the otherwise black umbra.

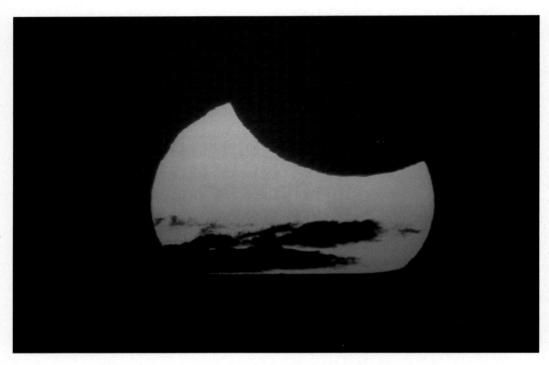

Plate 9   This photograph, by Bob Cooper of Canberra, nicely captures the mood of a solar eclipse at sunset.

The golden age 10

*The course of Total Eclipse Expeditions,
like that of true love, seems never to run
smooth. Of the three which the British
Astronomical Association has organized,
the first was baffled by cloud, the second
was hampered but not thwarted by
plague, and the third was hindered but
not beaten by war.*
E W MAUNDER, *The total solar
eclipse of 1900*

Francis Baily was born on 28 April 1774 in the quiet Berkshire village of Newbury. He showed an early aptitude for the sciences, and an interest in the world about him which led him to explore almost the entire United States of America when he was in his early 20s, no trivial pursuit at that time of slow transport when much of the west had barely been opened up. His career was, however, in the Stock Exchange, and at this he was sufficiently successful to retire, a very wealthy man, at the age of 51.

Long before retirement Francis Baily had developed a keen interest in astronomy and related sciences. He was one of the principle movers in the creation of the Royal Astronomical Society, and was later to become its President. One of his earlier pieces of astronomical research, published in 1811, was to calculate the circumstances of ancient solar eclipses for comparison with the classical records. This interest led him to observe eclipses, although the opportunity to travel was denied him for many years by his business commitments. He was not able to view the annular eclipse of 1820 for this reason, watching only a partial eclipse from Britain.

It turned out that there were few total or annular solar eclipses of easy access to Baily after his retirement. More than a decade was to pass before he could view an annular eclipse, and his ambition to see a total eclipse was not to be satisfied for a further six years.

Notwithstanding that Baily was but an educated amateur astronomer, that he was short-sighted, and that he had turned three score years before he was to witness a solar eclipse from its central line, Baily alone was the man who revived the study of eclipses by professional astronomers, a study which had faded out after Halley's death. Baily initiated the golden age of eclipse research. In this chapter that age will be described: a period which plucked the endeavour from the relatively uninformed observations of the an-

73

10.1   This engraved portrait of Francis Baily is
dated from about the time he ventured on his
first eclipse expedition. © Royal Astronomical
Society Archive.

cient and Middle Ages to culminate in 1919 in an observation of
fundamental importance to all of science.

In 1836 an annular eclipse was visible from the border regions of
Scotland and England. Francis Baily travelled to the town of Jedburgh,
and set up his 2⅝ inch (6.8cm) telescope in the garden of James
Veitch, about half a mile to the south. He observed the entire event,
and later described a singular phenomenon just at the moment of
central eclipse. For several seconds he saw the mountain peaks of the
moon, which were silhouetted against the sun, drawn out to meet the
edge of the sun and so divide up the slender ring of light into a series
of discrete blobs.

Baily wrote a lengthy report of his observations, and this was
published in the *Memoirs of the Royal Astronomical Society*. In it he also
collected together all previous reports of the phenomenon he could
find, none as detailed as his, quoting references from the annular
eclipses of 1736, 1748, 1791 and 1820, and from the total eclipses of
1715 and 1806. On some occasions the bright spots had been seen to
move, flowing into one another like droplets of mercury. The motion

Annular Eclipse of the Sun, May 15th 1836. See Page. 5.

Fig. 1.   Fig. 2.

10.2   Francis Baily's sketch of the beads at the 1836 annular eclipse of the sun, as published in the Memoirs of the Royal Astronomical Society.

of the moon across the sun is too slow to cause the spots of light to move in that manner, and we now know that their apparent movement is produced by turbulence in the earth's atmosphere—the shimmering that astronomers refer to as 'seeing'. The spots of light seen at total and annular eclipses are now universally called Baily's beads, whether or not they appear to move or change.

Sometimes, as Halley described in 1715, a single, prominent bead is separately seen: this is called the diamond ring effect. The first description of the diamond ring belongs with the French chronicler Honorius observing the 1133 eclipse. The moon does not keep precisely the same face towards us, continuously performing a small wobble so that different mountain peaks are brought into profile at the edge. It is tedious to predict exactly where the peaks and hollows will occur, so the computations are not normally undertaken, with the result that Baily's beads and the diamond ring remain two of the alluring surprises of total eclipses of the sun.

Baily's report attracted considerable attention, primarily because of its scholarly style. In particular, the Astronomer Royal, George Airy, concluded that it would be appropriate to investigate this and other effects related to eclipses at the next opportunity. It happened that no suitable solar eclipse near to British soil was to take place until 8 July 1842. Airy and Baily both observed that eclipse in Italy, the former from Turin, the latter, alone, from the window of a small room in the University of Pavia. In so doing, Baily realised a lifelong ambition— to see at first hand a total eclipse of the sun.

At the 1842 eclipse, Baily and Airy both saw the beads, but both were much more impressed by the other features they saw—the corona and in particular the prominences. Baily revealed a little of the emotions that had surfaced for him as they do for all observers:

> Splendid and astonishing, however, as this remarkable phenomenon really was, and although it could not fail to call forth the admiration and applause of every beholder, yet I must confess that there was at the same time something in its singular and wonderful appearance that was appalling, and I can readily imagine that uncivilised nations may occasionally have become alarmed and terrified at such an object.

It is apparent that Airy, at least, had not done his homework. He was surprised by the prominences, even though they had been beautifully described on previous occasions, particulary in the Swedish records of 1733. His interest was, however, heightened. When the 1851 eclipse traversed northern Europe, Airy was instrumental in setting up a major expedition. Had Francis Baily been alive, he would surely have been a member of the party. Airy gave guidelines for the observers, particularly specifying measurements that would establish the nature of the corona and prominences.

10.3 George Airy, Astronomer Royal at the time of the 1842 and 1851 solar eclipses, poses without his spectacles, though his myopia probably prevented him seeing the artist. The original photograph suffered an encounter with ink spots; two of which landed precisely on his eyes. © Royal Astronomical Society Archive.

Speculation on their nature was rife. Those who had witnessed the 1842 total eclipse inclined to the view that the 'rose-coloured mountains' were attached to the sun, though the implied sizes were frighteningly large, dwarfing our planet. Others reckoned that gases escaping from the moon were backlit by the sun. A few people even subscribed to the view that they were formed in the earth's atmosphere. Similar uncertainty surrounded the corona, to which some little thought had been given for more than two centuries. Kepler, seeing the corona in 1620, thought it to be the lunar atmosphere, while Halley, in 1715, deemed it more likely to be solar. By 1851 a sizeable minority believed it to arise solely within our own atmosphere, and fully expected it to assume different shapes when viewed from different locations.

To ensure a higher probability of clear weather, and to test whether the corona changed form with position, observers were despatched to various points along the eclipse track. Most of those sited in Norway were able only to describe the effect a total solar eclipse has on an overcast sky. Sufficient observations were collected to suggest, but not quite to convince, that the moon moves over the prominences, progressively covering up those on one side and uncovering those on the other. Despite the first successful use of photography to give a permanent record for more leisurely study, similar observations of the corona were much less conclusive, for it has fewer distinct features by which to judge the moon's motion. Questions, in short, remained to be answered, and scientists set themselves the task of answering them. They began to seek out total eclipses with enthusiasm.

Travel remained a tedious and an expensive business. The journey half way round the world for the 26 March 1857 eclipse in Australia was beyond the means of most astronomers. In any case, a local minister reported an overcast sky. 'The appearance of Sydney and her people was one which gave the idea of something terrible about to come upon them. This appearance was much heightened by the volumes of low-lying smoke that were being poured out just above the houses.'

Astronomers from Chile went to Peru for the eclipse of 30 November 1853, and the Emperor of Brazil sent his astronomers to the 7 September 1858 eclipse, but nothing of substance came from these expeditions, so it was not until 1860 that the science was advanced.

The Astronomer Royal gave instructions once more: 'Cosmically it is of the utmost importance to determine whether these appearances are attached to the sun or to the moon'. Observers were despatched to various parts of Spain in time for 18 July, when totality would sketch its line through the north of the country. The visitors had to compete

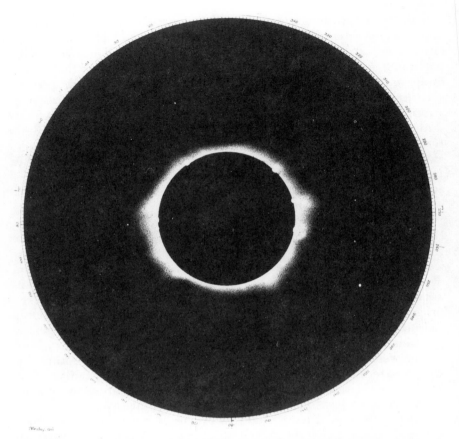

10.4   The first photograph of a solar eclipse, dated 1851, was a Daguerrotype. Here it has been copied as an engraving and is reproduced courtesy of the Royal Astronomical Society.

for accommodation with the many who escaped from Madrid in search of cooler regions at that time of year.

The eclipse track of 1860 began in the eastern Pacific, and crossed the USA and Canada before traversing the entire Atlantic Ocean to end in Spain. On this occasion American astronomers got in on the act. On 15 June the Senate and House of Representatives 'in Congress assembled' resolved that the Superintendant of the United States Coast Survey be 'directed to furnish a vessel and provisions for the conveyance to the most suitable point on the eastern coast of this continent for observing the total eclipse...of astronomers, not exceeding five in number, and their assistants'. The party made for the coast of Labrador where, not surprisingly, cloud blotted out most of their view. A report of their findings was buried in a bottle at Eclipse Harbour; another copy was buried in an obscure astronomical journal!

A more successful party sailed to the west coast, and a third undertook an epic journey by stagecoach, paddle steamer and birchbark canoe into the virtually unexplored waterways of Saskatchewan in Canada. By a superhuman effort they got into the path of totality just in time. The party included a zoologist named Scudder who later became a famous entomologist. Scudder classified the only wildlife he could find—several distinct species of mosquito—and bemoaned that the expedition after suffering many hardships could only 'sit in a marsh and view the eclipse through clouds'.

Greater success came to the British teams in Spain. Due in part to the use of photography, the solar origin of the prominences was finally and unequivocally proved, and plans could now be laid to study them in greater detail. It was the spectrograph, the astronomer's most powerful tool, that was to explore these huge formations. Spectrographs require more light than direct viewing, because the light is dispersed into its consitituent colours. Hence larger telescopes became necessary. By the time of the next major eclipse expeditions, in 1868, astronomers from several countries were encumbering themselves with massive pieces of equipment which had to be transported, housed, erected, tested, used, dismantled and returned. Far from the simple experiment that Baily had undertaken in 1836 with his own small telescope, these expeditions became the most demanding and expensive undertakings astronomers were to involve themselves with until the heyday of the giant reflecting telescopes.

The scent of discovery was in the air, and national pride found its feet. Large sums of money were made available for transporting astronomers and their equipment to the sites of total eclipses, irrespective of the remoteness. Few eclipses were ignored if their tracks of totality touched terra firma somewhere along their length, so the chosen few astronomers found themselves in the most outlandish of places, frequently with inadequate maps and no travel guides to smooth their passage. Typically, half of the time clouds foiled the observations, but expeditions usually returned with reports that added substantially to our knowledge of the particular corner of the globe they had visited. Many an expedition generated commentary enough to occupy a book this size and provide good reading throughout, giving a view of far-flung regions through the perceptive eyes of scientists. Some of these expeditions also marked milestones in our understanding of the sun.

The 1868 French expedition to India triumphed under the leadership of Pierre Janssen. On 15 November they demonstrated that the prominences largely comprised hydrogen gas, whilst the British, under Norman Lockyer, found an additional component in them which was then unknown on earth. They named it after the Greek word for the sun—*helios*—and to this day we call the element helium. Janssen demonstrated that the prominences were bright enough to be detected outside of eclipse with the use of a spectrograph. He made this discovery on the day after the eclipse. Meanwhile Lockyer, back in England, unknowingly explored the same idea, and actually succeeded on the very day that news of Janssen's work arrived.

Lockyer and Janssen both featured in the 1870 eclipse, which crossed southern Europe. Lockyer headed for Sicily, but his vessel HMS *Psyche* was wrecked on the coast. Fortunately both Lockyer and the expensive equipment were saved. Janssen faced even greater

10.5   This exquisite drawing of the 1871 eclipse was made from a series of photographs taken by Lord Lindsay's assistant, one Mr Davis.

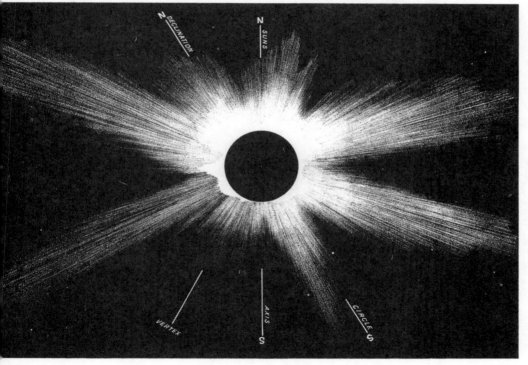

10.6 Compare these two drawings, made by different observers, of the corona of the
1874 eclipse. It was not until about the turn of the century that photographs clearly
superseded drawings, and showed that the corona changes only very slowly.

difficulties, for Paris was a city under siege at the height of the Franco-Prussian war. Determined not to be beaten, Janssen commandeered a hot air balloon and made a daring escape, with his equipment, to north Africa. His flight was successful, but his chosen site for viewing the eclipse was not, and he recorded only clouds.

'Disappointment is so often the lot of the astronomer', wrote the Oxford don H.H. Turner following another cloudy eclipse two decades later, 'that if he cannot cheerfully contemplate reverses it is not for want of practice'. On another occasion Turner referred to the 'terrible feeling of depression' following a cloudy eclipse. This feeling presumably was shared by each organisation that funded an expedition, and by those who paid the astronomers' salaries. It was estimated that three man-years of effort went into every eclipse expedition.

The eclipse of 29 July 1878 was well studied from Denver, Colorado, even though there were complaints that the dry air caused the wooden frames of cameras to shrink, risking light leaks. The

10.7   Equipment used at the 1878 solar eclipse in Colorado. 'Around it we erected a tent 14 feet in diameter made of canvas and scantling poles, with a tarpaulin stretched across a moveable beam for a roof.'

Pennsylvania State Railroad offered half price fares between the east coast and Denver for scientists going to view the eclipse, and combined with a comparable discount on the passage across the Atlantic on the White Star Line, British astronomers could make the journey for £34. Few however ventured it, and the major work was undertaken by American expeditions. On this occasion the observers sought and found the predicted but elusive intra-Mercurial planet Vulcan.

The planet Mercury is rarely seen because it never ventures far from the glare of the sun. The observations that had been made by the middle of the 18th century indicated that it did not quite obey Newton's gravitational laws as it orbited the sun. An interior planet, whose additional gravitational pull could disturb Mercury's path, was first proposed by Urbaine Leverrier, the French mathematician whose analysis of the motion of Uranus led to the discovery of the next planet beyond, Neptune.

A planet, especially a small one, lying much closer to the sun would be quite undetectable under the normal course of events. The astronomers thus argued that an abnormal event—a solar eclipse— offered the only sure way to find any such planets. The 1878 eclipse proved particularly fruitful, for they were able to discover not one, but two or three. The name Vulcan had already been suggested by Leverrier, but now more names were thought necessary.

Before the names could be bestowed, confirmatory observations were needed. The eclipses of the next few years were used for the confirmations, and in 1882 observers in Egypt were rewarded by the discovery of a bright comet that had sneaked in unannounced and undetected. Comets quite often are first spotted at total solar eclipses, the first certain case being in 418 AD. Vulcan and its mates were, however, stubbornly reluctant to make a new appearance. To cut short a long story, we now know that there are no intra-Mercurial planets. The peculiarities of Mercury's motion were beautifully accounted for by Einstein's Theory of Relativity.

The 1883 eclipse played no small part in opening up the beautiful Pacific archipelago of the Caroline Islands, a region almost unknown before the expeditions landed there. Then followed one in 1886 in the West Indies, which experienced weather like the curate's egg and a series of disasters, including breakage of some equipment, two policemen standing in front of another piece of equipment during totality, and the seizure of photographic plates by customs officials.

For the 1887 event the Europeans went to Russia and almost all were clouded out whereas the Americans tried Japan and had cloud-free skies, though one group still got no data because a volcano erupted just before the eclipse and blotted out the sun!

Another chance occurred just before Christmas 1889. Expeditions aimed for the two extremities of the track to compare photographs of the corona and so lay to rest the myth that our atmosphere contributes to its appearance. In Angola the British expedition was clouded out, while in the West Indies they were rewarded with good weather, but one of the most experienced members of their team contracted dysentry and died.

Observations of the corona had now covered more than two of the 11-year sunspot cycles, and astronomers were beginning to recognise that the general form the corona took varied with that cycle, being long at sunspot minimum and rounder at maximum spottiness.

The first occasion that all expeditions were successful was 16 April 1893, in sites as remote as Chile, Brazil and West Africa. This was then followed by a lean period. The eclipse of 9 August 1896 crossed from northern Norway to Japan, and most astronomers sought the latter only to be clouded out. From the island of Hokkaido H.H. Turner lamented 'Three huts in their enclosure (necessary to keep away dogs and fowls) . . . are standing the rain well'. He continued 'my poor golf clubs have not been taken out of their case; I never saw a more abjectly hopeless country for the game'.

Some limited success was had on the Norwegian coast, a place where one Colonel Burton Brown noted that 'such trifles as sleeping accommodation, attendance, and perhaps food, suitable for ladies, must be taken with them'.

The only truly successful expedition in 1896 was a small private party led by Sir George Baden Powell who took a few astronomers in his yacht, the *Otaria*, to the most unlikely spot to find clear skies, Novaya Zemlya off the northern coast of Siberia.

'Owing to the spread of plague in the country districts around Poona the Eclipse Committee had been compelled to entirely recast their plans.' The words, including the split infinitive, were those of Sir William Christie, Astronomer Royal, and referred to the great eclipse of 22 January 1898. India remained the favoured spot, and several sites were selected away from plague-infested centres, most of them involving the clearing of dense jungle. At Sahdol the team uncovered the remains of an ancient city. Light diversion was provided courtesy of the local Rajah who lent an elephant, but the Englishmen soon tired of riding it.

In 1900 the British had less of a trip to undertake. 'Algiers is astonishingly close to London—you can leave London at 11am on Sunday . . . and arrive at Algiers at 3pm on Tuesday.' Other British teams journeyed to Spain and Portugal, and the Portuguese Government encouraged astronomers by offering them free railway tickets. A team in Spain selected the roof of a stone tower as their observation platform, only to receive complaints from the more corpulent

10.8   Observers in Spain pose shortly before totality commences, 1900.

members of the party about the narrow access stairway. The USA offered yet another site. One European team went to North Carolina; its leader, perhaps having read too many westerns, requested an army guard for his astronomers. He didn't get it, but was offered instead free first-class passage by the Pennsylvania State Railroad.

For 1901 the choice locations were Mauritius or Sumatra. 'On Friday the 8th of March, after a most pleasant meeting of the Royal Astronomical Society, and dinner afterwards, I took my final orders from the Astronomer Royal near Charing Cross railway station at 12 o'clock at night', wrote J. J. Atkinson. As usual, some folks fared well and others poorly. 'The most exasperating part of it all', wrote the great American observer E. E. Barnard, 'was perhaps, the fact that if instead of going away off into the interior to search for good weather, we had simply gone ashore from the gunboat that carried us to Sumatra, and put up our instruments on the sea-shore near it, we should have had successful observations.' Some of the Americans reported sleeping in giant four-poster beds without covers but surrounded by mosquito netting. They also made a cryptic reference to saving an Englishman from drowning in his bath!

In Mauritius the team leader, E.W. Maunder, contracted fever, and his wife developed his eclipse photographs for him. Maunder noted how common rainbows were in Mauritius, and added that some observers saw one during the eclipse. The rainbow was noticeably different from the normal variety, and included a bright pink line along its length. This can probably be attributed to the hydrogen light given off by the prominences and chromosphere. The same phenomenon was seen by several observers at the eclipse of 12 October 1977 near Bogota, Colombia.

The choice of venues was greater in 1905. American and Canadian teams went to Labrador again, despite its reputation for bad weather. Spain proved a disappointment, and also demonstrated that weather has no respect for social position as the King of that country was denied a view at Burgos. Algeria and Tunisia were better favoured, but the indomitable British went to Aswan in Egypt. The eclipse date was 30 August, about the hottest Egypt can offer and surely fodder for Noel Coward's 'Mad dogs and Englishmen go out in the midday sun'! 'The water in a disused bath', wrote one cheerful astronomer, 'in which a few thousand bricks have been soaked for building our piers, is preferred for drinking to the unadulterated Nile itself.' Used in this sense, a pier is the support for a telescope.

After the success of 1905 it was only natural to expect failure in

10.9 Correct dress for eclipse expedition members early this century.

1907, particularly for a track of totality through Mongolia and Siberia in January. Observers stayed on the railway line near Samarkhand in conditions utterly opposed to those in Aswan, and witnessed a goodly snowfall.

By the quirks of the sun and moon, emphasis now shifted to the south Pacific, to the advantage of Australian astronomers. F.K. McClean led two expeditions, a cloudy one to the west coast of Tasmania in 1910 but a successful one two years earlier to a tiny coral atoll known as Flint Island. At the latter, McClean's party had to contend with a coral reef which wrecked their boats, tropical downpours that soaked everything, and, worst of all, the giant land crabs.

'Several members soon became skilled in the art of boot-making with pieces of carpet owing to the sharpness of the coral, considerably assisted by the ravenous propensities of the various crabs', wrote McClean. 'Our steward had part of his trousers eaten up in this way.' It seems that tying up the crabs with rope was ineffective, for they merely bit through it; wire served the purpose no better, for the crabs happily severed their tethered leg.

Measles, rather than the plague, caused a slight shift of venue

10.10 The setting of the 1908 Australian eclipse expedition to Flint Island appears idyllic, but this photograph fails to show the giant land crabs.

for the eclipse of 28 April 1911, for which teams converged on the Tongan island of Vavau. They vied for the sites which required fewest coconut palms to be felled; line honours unquestionably went to the Australians, who scored the local cricket pitch which was about to be converted into a palace for King George Tubou II.

Arthur Stanley Eddington appears on the scene in 1912. Acclaimed by many as the greatest astrophysicist of his time—perhaps of all time—Eddington was to become, a decade later, the first person to understand the interiors of stars, and how and why they function. His work was guided by that incomparably important analysis of physics by Albert Einstein, the Theory of Relativity. In 1912, however, he was one of many to go to Brazil and bring home nothing but memories. Eddington's party set up near a railway line, and the Brazilian authorities laid on a special engine between their accommodation and the observing site. Eddington noted 'the problem of how ten to twenty scientists can be placed on a light engine, so that each shall have a foothold, presented less difficulty than might be expected, but the general appearance caused much amusement to the native inhabitants.'

This cloudy visit to Brazil marked the beginning of a hiatus in eclipse expeditions. The next eclipse took place on 21 August 1914, in western Russia. Sixteen days earlier World War I had begun. Astronomers en route to the eclipse turned back, some of them finding the course of their ship now leading through minefields. Several

10.11   One of the eclipse camps in Tonga, 1911.

10.12   This special clock was designed to monitor the progress of the 1911 total eclipse, which lasted 217 seconds. The countdown to the eclipse comprised: −10 mins: bugle 'Rouse up'; −5 mins: bugle 'Alert'; −42 secs: 3 whistles; −9 secs: 2 whistles; −4 secs: 1 whistle; zero: voice 'Go'.

German astronomers invited to the Crimea by the Russian authorities were taken prisoner. Some of the equipment sent out by American parties was not returned for more than four years.

Despite the war, a few scientists had time for a little research. Eddington was one of them. He devoted himself particularly to Einstein's theory, being one of the few to recognise the full significance of it. A much-recounted anecdote relates Eddington being told that he must be one of the three men in the world who understood Relativity. When Eddington demurred he was told not to be modest 'On the contrary,' replied Eddington, 'I am trying to think who the third person is.'

10.13 Arthur Eddington, as sketched by Augustus John. Courtesy The Master and Fellows of Trinity College, Cambridge.

An unexpected prediction of Relativity was that light does not travel in straight lines, even through a vacuum, in contrast to what we are normally taught at school. When passing near a very heavy object, the path of light curves slightly. As Figure 10.14 shows, a light ray passing by the sun bends so that it appears to have come from a slightly different direction. As a result, if the sun passes close to the line of sight to a star, the star will appear shifted from its normal place as if repelled by the sun. The effect grows weaker for stars further out, and can really be measured only within a few degrees of the sun.

During the war years Eddington drew attention to the fact that these measurements could be made during, and only during, a total eclipse of the sun. Indeed, one astronomer who made it to the 1914 eclipse had tried the experiment, but had failed. The glow of the corona meant that there had to be a number of quite bright stars around the sun. Once a year the sun passes through a cluster of bright stars known as the Hyades, in the constellation Taurus. It does so near the end of May, so that would be the best of all times to attempt the crucial test of Relativity theory, Remarkably, the next observable total eclipse, in 1919, was due on 29 May.

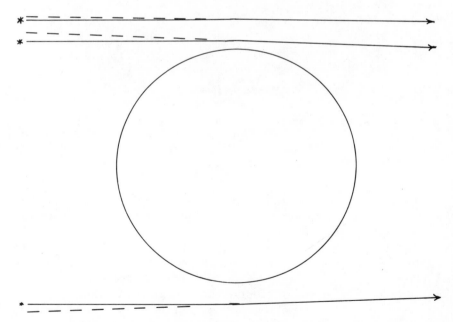

10.14 This exaggerated view illustrates the bending of light around the sun predicted by Einstein's Theory of Relativity. The stars, which normally lie in the directions of the continuous lines, are displaced when the sun intervenes to appear along the broken lines.

Here the Astronomer Royal, Sir Frank Dyson, entered the scene. He made representation to the British authorities to have Eddington spared the draft so that he would be able to lead an expedition to test Einstein's theory. Without Dyson, Eddington would not have attempted the measurement, simply because he was so utterly convinced of the truth of Einstein's theory that he didn't deem verification to be necessary.

The war ended and the expedition could be mounted. Eddington went to Principe, a small island in the Gulf of Guinea; A.C.D. Crommelin sailed to Sobral in Brazil. Both teams had usable weather, though Eddington observed through thin clouds and Crommelin's camera, designed for night-time work, went slightly out of focus when pointed at the sun.

It took 5 months for the observers to analyse the results, though this in part was due to the need to stay at their observing stations until they could photograph the same star field with the same cameras at night. Only by comparison of the two sets of plates could the subtle effects be detected.

The Royal Society and the Royal Astronomical Society held a joint meeting on 6 November 1919, and at this Dyson, Eddington and Crommelin announced the results: the deflection predicted by Einstein's theory was verified. The headlines bore the news across Britain and around the world, and many people for the first time in their lives learnt of Einstein's new explanation of the world around them. It was after this very meeting that the anecdote involving Eddington, recounted a few paragraphs above, took place.

The year 1919 does not mark the end of professional eclipse expeditions, but it can be seen as the end of the golden age. Gradually the work that could only be done during a total eclipse in an outlandish place was completed, and scientists found ways of studying the sun's corona and prominences on a regular basis. The first photograph of the corona outside eclipse was taken by the French astronomer Lyot in 1932, from the Pic du Midi Observatory in the Pyrenees, and today earth-orbiting satellites monitor it almost continuously.

There have been some occasional revivals of interest. The 1973 eclipse attracted a number of expeditions because of its exceptionally long duration—over 7 minutes. On this occasion a few astronomers were given an unique opportunity: the very first prototype Concorde supersonic airliner was flown along the eclipse track, and holes were cut in its fuselage to permit observations. By following the moon's shadow, the astronomers were treated to 74 minutes of continuous totality.

We cannot readily appreciate the difficulties experienced on eclipse expeditions during that golden age. The astronomers laboured often

91

in extreme heat and humidity, trying to get the delicate and sophisticated equipment that they had carted half-way round the world, and which was consequently always out of alignment if not actually broken, to work. They had to improvise many things, not least of which was a way to develop their photographs in temperatures higher than the chemicals were designed for. There were often difficulties in drying the photographic plates because of the humidity. Uneven drying would destroy the subtle features of the corona that they sought, and plates left wet for even a few minutes often were damaged by the large numbers of mosquitoes and beetles that landed on them and became stuck.

Total eclipses are by their very nature tense affairs, and the tension is that much greater when all you will have to show for half a year's work is the data you gather in those scant moments of totality. Science, too, always demands that this time you learn more than last time, applying more pressure to succeed than is reasonable. Then the fickle weather plays its role in creating greater tension.

One observer from the 1926 expedition to Sumatra aired his thoughts some time after the event when the pressure was off but the memory of it lingered: 'Benkoelen has a warm reputation, and the damp heat day and night reduced even the strongest to perspiration and profanity.' We glimpse another of the difficulties from the 1929 eclipse in Thailand: a special doctor was assigned to each expedition and was equipped with the full range of snake-bite sera. We can perhaps sympathise with astronomer X of whom it was reported in 1860: 'By one of those inadvertencies which oppressed almost every observer during the excitement of the eclipse, X forgot to withdraw the coloured glass from his eyepiece and actually observed the red prominences through it.'

As a closing remark on the business of professional eclipse expeditions, we can do no better than quote verbatim an essay topic from an 1896 Oxford University examination paper. Candidates were asked to enlarge on the theme: 'Photography has been of great avail in photographing Total Eciples' [sic].

Reminiscences of our first eclipse 11

For the world was built in order
And the atoms march in tune,
Rhyme the pipe and Time the warder,
The sun obeys them and the moon.
RALPH WALDO EMERSON, *Monadnock*

In March 1970 we were living in Minneapolis, at the heart of the North American continent. We had wintered there, experiencing temperatures we had previously only read of in books. In the heat of a sunny January day the mercury might have climbed to −10°F, a figure which sounds yet more gruesome on the celsius scale: −23°. In the unheated dome of the University's telescope the night-time chill dropped below −30°F. Even these temperatures failed to freeze out the warm, unpleasant aroma of the grain mills, a scent that hung like a pall over the city.

March brought milder temperatures: snow that had fallen five months earlier emerged from its winter coat to bid farewell in grey puddles of slush and dirty rivulets that snaked across the sidewalks. Suddenly the humidity soared, and for the first time that winter we found cold seeping into our bones, the damp, penetrating cold of the thaw.

Our thoughts turned to warmer climes. The slender path of a total eclipse was to traverse the North American continent that month, a charcoal line sketched from the tropical Pacific Ocean across much of Mexico before it coursed up the eastern seaboard. The professional astronomers and the wealthy were venturing into the highlands of Mexico for a view; we, impecunious, eyed the eastern states. Clear sky was considered most likely in the southern state of Florida, and still pretty likely in Georgia, but things looked less good further north. Balancing the probability of clear skies with the state of our wallets, and finding rather few airports to lie on the path of totality, we booked a flight to Savannah, Georgia, on the eve of the eclipse.

Our flight left early in the afternoon. That morning we telephoned the US Meteorological Bureau. Efficient people that they were, the Bureau had prepared a special eclipse report. Savannah, they said, would be cloudy; prospects were actually better further north.

It took over 30 minutes on the phone—fortunately local calls were free—to renegotiate our tickets. Yes, there were vacancies on a flight to Norfolk, Virginia. We boarded the flight with little time to spare, bound for an unknown city and a celestial adventure for which we were quite unprepared.

To us, in March 1970, a total eclipse of the sun was just another of those experiences that life offered: something that we felt should be witnessed once so that one could say one had seen it. A chance to see the sun's corona too, something otherwise denied us.

We stepped out from the bustle of Norfolk's busy airport as a deliciously blue sky began to melt into darkness. Across the road we saw not the city we might have expected but the silhouette of dark woodland. A signboard proclaimed the region as Norfolk's botanical garden. Surely this had to be a better spot to watch a total solar eclipse than some dusty city street.

A short distance along the road stood a small motel. Amazingly, there was a vacancy. A slender, dark-haired girl behind the desk asked, in an almost incomprehensible southern drawl, 'Hev yu come t'see th' heeclipse?'

The day dawned perfectly clear. The weather bureau was vindicated, it seemed. We strolled into the botanical gardens, an unspoilt tract of native woodland threaded by paths that wound in and out amongst sparkling lakes. The gardens stretched to the Atlantic coast, and one inlet featured the hull of an old sailing ship. Eventually, having explored most of the gardens, we selected a seat beside one of the lakes, set up the camera, and waited.

Presently the sun became appreciably dented: the partial phase had begun. We had seen a few partial eclipses before, but not so many that the novelty had fully worn off, so we studied the growing scallop on its edge. Not a cloud dusted the sky, and our adrenalin was rising. A small group set up a telescope at the next park bench, but apart from them we could not see a soul.

A feeling that something was wrong began to come over us. The notch had appeared almost at the bottom of the sun's disc. We knew that the moon moves almost right-to-left across the sky—how could it possibly cross the centre of the sun from this starting point? Had we, after all, come to the wrong place? Was the airport not actually in the path of totality?

Half an hour passed, taking half a lifetime to do so. Quite a lot of the sun was covered now, but it still wasn't clear that totality would really reach us. The sun lay high in the sky by this time, and still no cloud dared to tarnish the sky. Savannah, we later learnt, sat under a heavy pall of cloud all that day.

The sun narrowed to a crescent like a two-day-old moon. The dappled light that filtered through a small tree near our bench now

clearly formed crescent spots on the gravel path. The air was noticeably cooler, too, and a breeze stirred for the first time, a furtive, shifting breeze that would blow for a few seconds only before pausing for rest or changing its line. Our adrenalin levels reached new peaks.

All shadows began to soften, to melt away. It was eerie. Something very wrong was happening. Light of this quality we recognise around sunset any clear day, but then the shadows stretch long and dark; now they lay short and pale, altogether wrong. An ominous silence hung heavily over the woodland. Across the lake a stand of tall, straight trees had shed their pastel colours and outline shadows to dissolve into a hazy grey backdrop. Suddenly the silence was pierced by two distant, dull booms—rocket-borne experiments launched from a nearby naval base to make sophisticated observations of the event that was now a scant minute away.

Tense, we waited. The light was failing perceptibly now, the sky darkening; the wind breathed cool on our cheeks. Still we had no comprehension of what was about to happen. In these closing seconds of sunlight we were still merely enjoying the eerie sight of the progressing eclipse. Moments later we were to find Nature plucking the strings of our emotions.

However ready one might feel to witness one's first total eclipse of the sun, whatever might have been read in advance, nothing can prepare the mind for the extraordinary experiences that are packed into a scant five seconds as totality commences. The very fact that even to decribe the events in speech takes nearer to three minutes dilutes the impact of the account.

In the last two seconds it seemed as though a giant hand had reached from somewhere and spun a variable rheostat control, the type one may use to dim room lights. Darkness—not the total dark of night, but the half light of sunset—poured over the scene. All shadows vanished, and the world around us grew flat and featureless. At that very instant a commotion arose from the lake, and a flight of ducks rose swiftly into the air to head off in various directions in search of their nightly roost. Poor, confused creatures, they had not the wit to look up. High in the sky sat a black circle seeming appreciably darker than any other part of the sky, and around one side of it ran a string of dazzling pinpricks of light, some brighter than others and all unevenly spaced. These were Baily's beads, strung for our enjoyment on a necklace 5000 kilometres in length.

The beads hung, poised around the moon's dark circle, as if time were momentarily arrested. Then, suddenly, all but one was extinguished. The stubborn bead persisted a scant second longer, then it too vanished, and immediately the eye became aware of the sun's corona completely encircling the moon. The corona was indisputably white, a pure, translucent, pearly white that faded imperceptibly into the deep blue sky. Never before had white seemed a colour one could describe as beautiful, but then never before had we seen so pure a white, nor any substance that seemed at once so rich and bright yet at the same time filmy and transparent.

More than just the colour gave beauty to the corona. It had texture. No part of it was uniform: throughout its breadth were threaded streaks and flows and lines, mostly radiating outwards from the sun. In some parts it stretched far; in others it faded quickly into the blue sky, so that its outline was ragged and curled.

At that instant we glimpsed our inner selves. Never before had we paid any real attention to the sun's presence. The sun had always risen and set according to the pattern we must have learnt as babes. Whether it lay behind sullen clouds or shone from an azure sky, the sun was reliably there, where it should be, when it should be. The pattern of night and day, of dark and light, was as regular and reliable as one could hope. Yet now, abruptly, the sun had been taken away in the middle of the day, at a time when darkness just doesn't happen. We stood in rapture viewing the sun's corona, yet in awe at the phenomenon. Things felt terribly, terribly wrong in a way that rational argument could not address. Like the ducks, some part of us wanted to dash off and hide, whilst competing within the same body was the urge to stare at the sky, with eyes riveted to the black circle and its delicate halo. We were witnesses to the extraordinary events that had so upset tiny pockets of mankind throughout recorded history, and at last could identify with their fears and confusion.

All of this we absorbed in those five incredible seconds. Only then, when the eclipse was clearly underway and the world had ceased to change at such a giddy rate, did we begin to explore the sight before us. We became aware of stars visible in the middle of the day, and of the bright planet Venus shining forth not far beyond the reach of the corona. We saw the strange orange glow that had settled just above the horizon. Finally, we saw the prominences.

Through the telephoto lens of the camera the prominences were exquisite. In contrast to the pearly white of the corona they shone a rich crimson—small flecks and flames that projected from behind the dark silhouette of the moon.

After 30 seconds the adrenalin flow had subsided a little and we could absorb the spectacle itself. We took photographs, even finding the time and composure to change lenses on the camera. Gradually the prominences had vanished from view, the only indication that the moon was still moving across the face of the sun. The group with the telescope called us over, and for a few seconds we were able to examine the incredible detail of the corona that was revealed through the eyepiece, a forest of fine threads.

Some prominences began to show on the lower right of the moon, a clear indication that soon the sun would appear from that quarter. Had three minutes really passed already?

The end of totality was accompanied by an involuntary gasp from all within earshot. In not more than a second an intense spot of light appeared and grew to utterly dazzling brilliance. Sunlight was pouring out through a single valley on the moon's limb. There was scarcely time to utter the words 'diamond ring' before the light burst forth from its tiny spot and rushed like water round one half of the dark moon. Suddenly the sun was a narrow crescent again. Totality had ended.

11.2　The diamond ring at the 1970 eclipse.

The process that had so held our fascination began its reversal. Within the grey forest of trees, ghostly shadows took form, and what had seemed a flat backdrop acquired depth and reality. One by one the ducks returned, each splashing down in the lake, ruffling its feathers indignantly, and settling unconcernedly into the water as if it had merely been away to stretch its wings.

The air temperature was appreciably rising again as we packed up our belongings. No longer had we the slightest interest in watching the closing stages of the partial phase, which now seemed utterly anticlimactic.

That afternoon the airport thronged with amateur astronomers and eclipse chasers. Cameras, telescopes and related equipment were piled in the departure lounge, and their excited owners gathered in little groups comparing notes. For some this was the fifth, sixth or seventh total eclipse. These veterans were able to compare the shape of the corona, never twice the same, with that of a decade earlier. We, the novices, absorbed their talk. When we had planned this trip it had seemed something to be done once in our lives; but already we could sense that this would not be our last eclipse expedition, that the high we had just experienced would demand to be repeated, that one day we too would compare notes at airports with others who had travelled the world in search of that all-too-brief moment of darkness.

Birds fell from the sky 12

Yet there is something round thy lips
That prophesies the coming doom,
The soft grey herald shadow ere the eclipse
Notches the perfect disc with gloom.
J R LOWELL, *On a portrait of Dante*

We have described our own reaction to a total eclipse of the sun in the best words we can, and it is time now to relate the experiences of others. Of course, some of the older eclipse accounts we quoted in chapters 8 and 9 clearly indicate the awe with which the ancient and mediaeval observers held eclipses of either body, but their words were few and much must have been left unwritten. When we look at the last hundred years we find more complete descriptions, many of which convey far more than the words we can find.

In these more detailed accounts we find reports of strange colours cast upon the terrain, and of the reactions of animals, birds, plants and insects to the sudden extinction of the sun. The mediaeval chronicler who claimed that birds fell from the sky probably didn't mean it quite literally, but responded to the fact that the birds which had been happily flying around before totality took themselves off to roost when it happened.

In examining the reactions of people to total solar eclipses we will inevitably be led to the business of tourism, which now is a blossoming industry. We can trace its development from tentative beginnings late last century when the prediction of eclipse tracks became commonplace.

One feature which we have not ourselves seen is the shadow bands. For a minute or so before totality, and again when the sun first appears, all illumination comes entirely from a very fine line of light where the sun protrudes from behind the moon. As this light shines through the earth's atmosphere, minute ripples in the air cause patterns to be projected onto the ground. They are akin to the bright and dark patterns which can be seen when sunlight shines through rippled water onto the bed of a stream, shallow lake or swimming pool. The air behaves very like water, but because it is much more tenuous the faint patterns are smeared out and rarely detectable when the light comes from a patch as large as the entire sun.

Just like a stream of water, the air flows and the faint patterns move with it. For a brief moment fuzzy streaks or ripples alternately light and dark, can be watched travelling by. The bands may be anything from metres to centimetres apart, and may either jostle and shimmer rapidly, or move with the wind at a brisk walking pace. If the breeze is stronger than that, the patterns tend not to form, or at least are not so easily recognised. They are most readily seen against a whitewashed wall or on an expanse of uniform pale ground.

These patterns are called shadow bands, though the name is misleading because they are not shadows of anything. Light that would have landed in the duskier parts has been deflected rather than obstructed by ripples of air, and lands instead in the brighter areas.

It is uncertain when the shadow bands were first seen. A discovery at the 1878 eclipse in Colorado has been claimed, but they were well described by observers at Perpignan during the 1842 eclipse, and may have been seen earlier.

During totality the shadow bands disappear, because the only source of illumination is the corona, an object even bigger than the sun. At that time the lighting is particularly bizarre, be it cloudy or clear.

George Airy, watching the 1842 eclipse under a sky dotted with clouds reported that 'a large cloud over our heads . . . became . . .

12.1 This rather idealised sketch of shadow bands on a wall was made by a Spanish observer in 1870 in the town of Terranova.

blacker, if possible, than pitch, and seemed to be descending rapidly; its aspect became terribly menacing, and I could almost imagine that it appeared animated.' Many other observers have noted that cloud seems to descend suddenly and dramatically, and have used adjectives like ominous and threatening. One is reminded, when reading these and other accounts, of the Mayan belief that some creature plunges headlong towards the earth during an eclipse.

If the cloud cover is solid, it acts as a screen on which the moon's shadow is projected. The huge black patch can be seen approaching, passing overhead and receding again. Captain Biddulph, watching the clouds from a mountain ridge at the 1851 eclipse, wrote:

> The rapidity of motion of the shadow . . . produced a feeling that something material was sweeping over the earth at a speed perfectly frightful. I involuntarily listened for the rushing noise of a mighty wind.

When clouds do not interfere, the shadow of the moon crosses land and sea, and within it lighting plays its own tricks. Summarising the events, E. W. Maunder wrote after the 1900 eclipse:

> The impressiveness of a total eclipse of the sun does not rest solely or even chiefly in the revelation of the corona, wonderful and unaccustomed though its appearance is. The daylight turned to darkness, being so different from that caused by a mist or fog, and distinguishable too from the gloom of a great storm cloud, has an unwonted effect which seems therefore to partake of the supernatural. And this effect is heightened by the strange colouring seen on land and sky. Every tint that seems to speak of life or warmth in the objects around fades out, and is replaced by the ghastly hue of decay. The flowers all look withered, the grass and trees exchange their living green for lead, the faces of the watchers lose all trace of health and become not merely wan but livid. Whilst above, the blue of the sky has changed to a deep almost black funereal purple, and round the horizon, where the light is much the strongest, there is a glow of an angry gold, a sulphur-light not untinged with red.

Of the 1860 eclipse one commentator noted: 'The metallic light of which I speak, acting upon the grass and foliage, produced a sepulchral sickly tinge which made the faces of those assembled look spectral and unearthly.'

Others have picked out very specific colours, and there is frequent reference to a greenish hue. In 1860 Mrs Airy noted even before totality began that 'a sickly green hue began to creep over the whole nearer landscape. A peculiar mournful sighing wind, cold and strong,

101

began to rise as if from among the large old trees beneath us on the north side of the hill.' Eighteen years earlier another observer described 'the extensive colouration of an unusual hue, that was visible, the rapid changes which occurred, above all the obscurity which settled over nature like the funereal pall thrown over a dead body, and whose subsequent withdrawal in an instant, operated like a resurrection.'

Wordsworth witnessed the annular eclipse of 1820 from Lake Lugarno, and wrote of '. . . something night and day between, like moonshine—but the hue was green.'

From the annular eclipse of 29 June 1033 we find the following description, made by monks at Elnon Abbey in France: 'His face looked green at first and then yellow, and then these colours were affected as gold or silver is usually affected when they are cleaned by being dipped in lead. Thereupon the clothes and faces of men looked as if they were yellow.' In 1900 an observer from Portugal commented on the contrast between the indigo sea and tawny-yellow sky.

Dark green and livid yellow—these are the terms used to describe eclipse lighting. What are we to make of them? It is certain that the corona is pure white, and provides most of the light—typically as much as the full moon. It cannot turn objects green, and one is led to suspect that the colours are in the eye of the beholder. Several physiological factors could cause such an effect, and they would vary from one observer to another.

If you stare at a room light for a while, then look away, you will see an after-image of it that typically will be greenish in hue. Observers who stare at the sun in the seconds before totality may be so affected, and perhaps even the corona itself is bright enough to cause this effect.

Another reason may be that it takes the eye some little while to adjust to the sudden drop in light level: during that adjustment its colour sensitivity may be disturbed.

Again, if the observers closed their eyes to avoid being dazzled by the shrinking patch of sunlight, they would have had a predominantly red light filtering through their eyelids. When darkness fell they would have opened their eyes and would by contrast have seen green.

Contrast can also account for a greenish hue in another way, because the sky near the horizon tends to be orange or yellow. If you study a grey object alongside an orange one, the grey will seem green.

Why is the horizon orange during totality? The diameter of the moon's shadow can range from a kilometre or less, to several hundred kilometres according to the circumstances of the eclipse. It has indeed been seen and photographed travelling across the ground from aircraft and space vehicles, the first occasion being in France on 17 April

1912. Standing within this shadow one can look to distant portions of the atmosphere which are sunlit, and these will appear yellow or orange according to their distance and the dustiness of the air. The horizon would normally appear orange on any clear day in fact, but for the amount of blue light superimposed on it from sunlight that lands more nearly overhead and is scattered across the sky.

While all of these mechanisms could be invoked to explain the old accounts of green hues during totality, we have ourselves seen yellow-green colours, and cannot account for them by any other means. The occasion was 23 October 1976 in Australia. This eclipse occurred shortly before sunset, and was viewed through thin cloud. At totality, of course, all eyes turned towards the sun. After a few moments we looked round to find behind us an extraordinary seascape. The distant sky to the east was painted in vivid yellows and greens, and those colours reflected in the rippled Pacific to produce a scene of striking beauty. We have never seen such colours in the sky on any other occasion. Perhaps Shelley captured it best, in *The Revolt of Islam*:

> *With hue like that when some great painter dips*
> *His pencil in the gloom of earthquake and eclipse.*

In modern times the reaction of ordinary mortals to a total eclipse has continued to be that of awe, if not downright terror. Norse fishermen in 1851 were described as terrified, but one wonders whether this was merely an attempt by the professionals to enhance their own images. Professional astronomers are never terrified, of course. It would, nonetheless, be a gross exaggeration to suggest that they are not awed. There are many records of astronomers bungling their experiments simply because they found the experience of the eclipse too devastating. As long ago as 1851, even before the eclipse of that year, the English astronomer Charles Piazzi Smyth drew attention to this fact:

> For its effects on the minds of men are so overpowering, that if
> they have never had the opportunity of seeing it before, they
> forget their appointed tasks of observation to witness the scene.
> Although it is not impossible, but that some frigid men of metal
> nerve may be found capable of resisting temptation, yet certain it
> is, that no man of ordinary feeling and human heart and soul, can
> withstand it.

Grammarians and students of the comma should note that we have repeated Smyth's punctuation exactly.

Smyth referred to men. Perhaps women are better equipped with metal nerve. One elderly Norwegian woman was seen to take no greater notice of that very eclipse than to light a candle and continue

103

with her work, never once glancing up to see what had happened to the sun. Around her the peasants and fishermen 'made off immediately, and tried to hide themselves from what they believed to be approaching destruction.' Again, Smyth would have to have been impressed by Miss Irene Maunder who helped her father out at the 1898 eclipse in Algiers.

'The colour faded from the sea and trees, a shouting and wailing arose from the square below, the light was fading; suddenly the moon slipped over the sun and the eclipse was total!' Did Miss Maunder look up? No—she worked carefully through her appointed tasks until:

> There! my photographs were taken, and now I could look up!
> I shall never forget the sight. A deep purple sky, a black globe,
> surrounded by a crimson glow, and above and below it a milk-
> like flame stretching its long streamers away into the purple. The
> darkness, the cold wind, the silent workers around me, and the
> shouting crowd below all tended to make this strange and
> glorious sight still more impressive, and I found myself
> stretching out my arms to that exquisite corona in perfect ecstacy.
> Suddenly the moon slipped off the other side of the sun, and out
> he shone in a blaze of light, or so it seemed in comparison with
> his eclipse. An Englishman cheered. Some Frenchmen clapped.
> Totality was over!

Shouting seems to be a pretty standard reaction to the end of totality. Francis Baily was 'astounded by a tremendous burst of applause from the streets below' as the 1842 eclipse ended. During totality itself, however, silence is the norm. The French astronomer Arago, watching the 1842 eclipse from Perpignan, was struck by the silence that fell like a heavy blanket over the crowd he estimated to number over 20 000. 'The phenomenon in its magnificence', he noted, 'had triumphed over the petulance of youth, over the levity which certain persons assume as a sign of superiority, over the noisy indifference of which soldiers usually make profession.'

In the Orient the populace tends to take the entire business more seriously. 'This proclamation is issued to command all the local civil and military authorities, gentry, merchants, and the people to protect the moon.' Thus wrote the Viceroy of Hong Kong before the lunar eclipse of 4 August 1906, and he continued 'I command you all not to disobey this proclamation.'

Astronomers on the 1898 eclipse expedition to India, were amazed by the impact the event had on the crowds. Fully 400 000 came to bathe in the sacred Ganga river at Varanasi (Benares). Because of the plague, comparable numbers were kept from doing the same in the sea along Black Bay, though a few did enter the water wearing Durab grass tied to their clothes as protection not from the epidemic but against the eclipse. Reuters reported that:

> Native astrologers had prophesied all kinds of calamities, including a tidal wave at Bombay, and some foretold a great disaster a week hence. Religious Hindus sat down and counted their beads at the moment of contact, at the same time reciting mantras, or prayers and hymns. Here and there on the foreshore stood Parsees, Zand-Avasta in hand, and with their faces turned towards the sun. The Brahmin priests, who are ever ready to receive alms, ceased their solicitations during the eclipse. Beggars, however, swarmed nearly everywhere, and the Hindu streets were alive with the cry 'Dedan sute Girhan', meaning 'Give alms for the recovery of the sun from the jaws of the dragon Rahu.'

In response to the same eclipse, the Nizam of Hyderabad released fifty prisoners and gave each a present of clothes and money.

Totality on 11 June 1983 covered much of the island of Java and thus provided eclipse fanatics with a glimpse of the Indonesian view of the affair. Huge posters depicting Kala Rau, an evil giant who devours the sun or moon, reminded people of past beliefs, but there was little superstitious reaction to Gerhana Matahari Total. The Indonesian Government was concerned about the possibility of widespread eye damage and thus forbade people to watch the event. The usually bustling city streets were empty save for the few police patrols who ensured that nobody violated the proclamation; instead people gathered around their television sets and watched totality on a clinical screen, thereby missing 90% of what a total eclipse really is. A well-educated Indonesian watched us observing the eclipse on a hotel roof, but though offered safe filters to view the partial phase, and though understanding that totality was perfectly safe to view, staunchly remained loyal to his Government and obeyed the proclamation.

Since total solar eclipses are such impressive spectacles, it comes as no surprise to learn that people are prepared to pay money to see one, and thus that others are waiting on the sidelines to take that money. Tourism has become a regular feature of total eclipses, and no decent event passes without several tours being arranged to the centre line. If the optimum viewing is at sea, then ocean liners are brought in on the act. For the splendid eclipse of 11 June 1973 no fewer than seven cruise ships were in use, the largest alone holding 1900 passengers. There is no difficulty in locating an eclipse expedition, so nobody need be denied the opportunity of getting to the central line provided that they have the will and the finance.

Tourism really began when eclipse tracks could be predicted with

105

sufficient accuracy. Edmond Halley was the first man to sketch the expected path of totality on a map, in this case of southern Britain. Obviously, those who lived on line of totality may well have made some attempt to witness the event, but this cannot be counted as tourism. Some of the first examples of tourism were, therefore, the wealthy gentlemen who were able to make their way independently to a suitable spot in 1715 or 1724.

Organised tourism, by which we mean that some entrepreneur planned the excursion and then sold tickets to the public, began in the late 19th century. An early example was the eclipse of New Year's day 1889. For this, special trains took the venturesome from San Francisco or Sacramento to a spot where the path of totality intercepted the railroad line. In the year 1900, no fewer than 20 000 rail excursion tickets to the centre line were sold in Madrid.

The tourist industry demonstrated two opposite reactions to the 1905 eclipse. On the one hand an Italian steamship company offered ten-day cruises to Palma, Majorca, for the very reasonable price of £8-£10 inclusive of food and accommodation. At the other extreme, bed and breakfast in Burgos, Spain, set people back by the princely sum of £4 on the eve of totality.

Further interest in eclipses was spurred following the successful 1922 event at Wollal in northwestern Australia. The various expeditions pooled their results to made a one-hour film of the eclipse, and this showed for several weeks at the Royal Albert Hall in London. Ten years later some of those who saw the film were able to join a tour across the Atlantic to the eclipse of 31 August 1932, a tour that took in the Canadian Rockies, Grand Canyon, Meteor Crater and other scenic highlights in addition to a cloudy eclipse in Maine. This was the first undertaking of such magnitude that had been linked to an eclipse, but is typical of the tours available today.

So primeval is the impact of a total eclipse that we should expect animals to feel it too. Indeed, we have already commented on the behaviour of the ducks at the site of our first total eclipse. Edmond Halley made passing reference to this after the 1715 eclipse: 'Nor shall I trouble you with the concern that appeared in all sorts of animals, birds, beasts and fishes, upon the extinction of the sun, since ourselves could not behold it without some sense of horror.'

Very many descriptions have been given of the reactions of animals and even of plants, and some of the early professional expedition reports included studies of them. There is general, but not universal, agreement on the reactions. The poet Alfred Noyes summarised it when one of his characters saw 'the weirdly punctual shadow creep across the sun, bewildering all the birds with thoughts of evening.'

Certainly most total eclipses are of long enough duration that daytime birds go to roost and nocturnal creatures come out briefly. Many observers have noticed how swallows vanish from the air at totality, while pigeons and hens make quickly for their shelters. Owls and bats appear, cicadas burst into song, grasshoppers fall silent, and cockerels crow. Earthworms and snakes come out, while bees make for their hives. Sparrows, fussy by nature, normally spend a considerable period twittering noisily before settling down for the night; at eclipses they never have the time to progress beyond the twittering phase. Other birds which traditionally sing by day fall silent, and those which prefer to sing in the dark, such as the nightingale, deem it dark enough to let loose a few notes. All these seem to be normal reactions to darkness.

Not all reactions are normal, however. Chickens have been reported to start fighting, while crows and gulls tend to fly around in circles. These are the responses of confused or frightened creatures, best exemplified, perhaps, by a herd of cattle which formed itself into a circle, facing outward. Cats sometimes seek the comfort of a favourite human companion, and may begin to mew pitifully. Grazing horses have been reported to show no reaction at all, but those in harness usually refuse to work, either standing on the spot or lying down.

Rarely is disinterest reported among animals, not merely because this would fail to be newsworthy, for scientific reports rarely make

12.2 Professional astronomers around the turn of the century studied the impact of eclipses on all forms of flora and fauna. They were particularly amused by this response by Spaniards in 1900.

news anyway, but because disinterest is genuinely uncommon. One such example from 1851 relates how a wagtail continued feeding its young during totality. Parents of young children can probably sympathise with the poor bird. Another species which generally ignores the event is the humble ant.

Whether or not plants react depends on their normal speed of closing up at dusk. Some, for instance Mesembryanthemum, anemone, gentian and crocus, close fully, while others remain open. One expedition noted that the night violet had time to release its nocturnal scent.

It might be expected that eclipses would have provided ample fuel for both literature and art, but in fact the body of material seems fairly slight. We have already used some of the examples that we find enjoyable throughout this book, so we'll mention only a few here.

One classic eclipse story can be found in Rider Haggard's famous *King Solomon's Mines*. If you have access to an early edition, you might dig it out and examine the relevant section. Haggard used the eclipse to provide a cover of darkness for a couple of hours, somewhat in excess of the seven minutes maximum duration available to him at that latitude. In later editions he revised the passage.

Eclipses tend to be mentioned in older literature more as omens or objects of fear, and usually only in brief allusion. Shakespeare provides a splendid example in *King Lear*:

> *These late eclipses in the sun and moon portend no good to us.*
> *Though the wisdom of nature can reason it thus and thus, yet*
> *nature finds itself scourged by the sequent effects: love cools,*
> *friendship falls off, brothers divide; in cities, mutinies; in*
> *countries, discord; in palaces, treason; and the bond cracked*
> *'twixt son and father.*

Milton has another in *Paradise Lost*:

> *. . . as when the sun, new risen,*
> *Looks through the horizontal misty air,*
> *Shorn of his beams; or from behind the moon*
> *In dim eclipse, disastrous twilight sheds*
> *On half the nations, and the fear of change*
> *Perplexes monarchs.*

Contrast the more modern response, from Shelley's *Prometheus Unbound*:

> *As in the soft and sweet eclipse,*
> *When soul meets soul on lovers' lips.*

We close this chapter with a few anecdotes to illustrate the human response to eclipses. All come from England, the first dated to the last total eclipse to cross that country, on 29 June 1927.

On that occasion the centre line etched its way through Lancashire and Yorkshire, and mostly landed on cloud, though the Astronomer Royal did get some patchy observations. Imagine a gaggle of eclipse veterans at afternoon tea prior to a meeting of the Royal Astronomical Society. Eavesdrop as they compare their experiences chasing the shadow line into romantic corners of the globe. The conversation turns to the Astronomer Royal's last expedition; he clears his throat, lowers his voice, and mumbles the name ... Giggleswick.

It is not too far from Giggleswick to Clitheroe, and there the licensee of the Moorcock Inn, one Walter Greenhalgh, successfully applied to extend his opening hours 'for the sale of intoxicants' to include the period 6 to 11am on the morning of the eclipse. We have no information on how much money the enterprising publican made from the extra hours, but we would love to have been a fly on the wall to find out what the presumably well-lubricated Lancashire lads made of the event.

Somewhat to the north, in Middlesborough, Peter Shrimpton was aged 91 when that eclipse passed over. He climbed 150 feet to the top of a bridge over the River Tees for a view of the eclipse. Unfortunately the cloud rose to a still greater elevation.

For the final anecdote let us look back further, to the previous cloudy eclipse over Britain, which was annular rather than total. On 15 March 1858 the Somerset town of Frome lay near the centre line, and the local inhabitants were out in force to watch the spectacle. One local wag paid the town crier to go round Frome announcing that because of the disappointment the eclipse would be repeated next year!

13 Observing eclipses

*Roses have thorns, and silver fountains
    mud;
Clouds and eclipses stain both moon and
    sun,
And loathsome canker lives in sweetest
    bud.
All men make faults.*
SHAKESPEARE, *Sonnet 35*

More than any other object, the moon is suited to that telescope you bought to look at Halley's comet and haven't used since. While there is considerable satisfaction to be had from studying it through binoculars, it is the telescope that really brings out detail in the grey-white disc.

The observer quickly learns that the best time to see the moon is not when it's nearly full, but around first or third quarter when the terminator, separating sunlit and dark portions, winds its contorted way across the disc.

What makes the moon so attractive is the surrealistic shadows cast by mountains and crater rims. Here on earth shadows are not black; even the deepest shade is lit by the blue sky, that cannot be excluded except within a cave. When the sun lies low near the horizon, and shadows are long, the sky softens them. On the moon however, there is no blue sky. No atmosphere surrounds the moon to smear sunlight across the sky. Only the earth is a secondary source of light, and by the time the moon reaches first quarter earthlight is pretty insignificant. Shadows, therefore, are jet black, in stark contrast to the bright sunlit mountains, craters and plains. The longer the shadows the more shapely and interesting. Because there are very few cliffs or other steep slopes on the moon, shadows are found only where the sun is low in the lunar sky: attention is thus focused on a narrow strip running up and down the terminator. The strip of interest is so narrow, and the height of the sun so critical to the shape of the shadows, that the scene rarely repeats. Each time you look at the moon there is something new to see.

Depending on the size of your telescope, the steadiness of the air, and your visual acuity, there are many features of interest. You will find that some craters have central mountains but others do not. Some are scarred by smaller craters that have been formed overlapping them; others have been flooded by lava and now show up as ghostly rings in the grey expanses. There are shallow mounds called domes, narrow meandering valleys called clefts or rilles, and a long, steep fault in the form of a step and called the Straight Wall. There have been contentious features too—a crater that was once believed to have changed shape, and a natural archway that subsequently was proved to be a result of the juxtaposition of shadows.

Sketching features on the moon has little scientific value now that satellites have mapped the surface in comprehensive three-dimensional detail. Nonetheless, it can be a satisfying and attractive artform. Reproduced here in Figure 13.1 are a couple of the pictures we have produced, albeit using a somewhat larger telescope than most readers of this book will have access to.

When it comes to observing an eclipse, the telescope no longer has so great an advantage over binoculars. What is of interest is not the detail within one crater, but the entire moon and the range of colours and intensities within the earth's umbra. The colours are made more prominent by a telescope or binoculars which feed more light to our eyes. At night the human eye loses much of its colour vision, giving

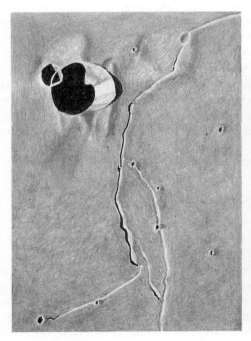
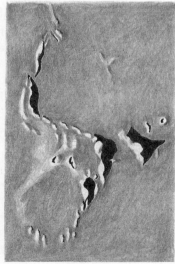

13.1   Two moonscapes, typical of the many views to be had through a good amateur telescope.

preference to the nerve endings that record faint light best, rather than those with colour sensitivity. If the eclipse is a dark one, the eye may have lost its acuity for colour. Then a pair of binoculars or a low-power telescope will boost the brightness so that the eye switches once more to its colour sensitivity. At high magnification the light is again too spread out and the colour is drab.

The progress of an eclipse is sufficiently slow that most will not want to watch it continuously; every 20 minutes or so is perfectly adequate to get a good feel for the changes. Enthusiasts keep a continual watch and note the time when the dark umbral shadow edge reaches and subsequently leaves prominent landmarks. From careful timing they can then compute the diameter of the shadow, which in turn leads to a diameter for the earth. This may seem a laborious way to estimate a quantity that you can look up in any atlas or astronomy text book, and in practice the diameter so estimated is invariably too big. This enlargement of the earth's shadow is caused by dust in the atmosphere, dust which may come from volcanic eruptions, bush fires or meteor showers. Thus we can use the eclipses to monitor subtle changes in the atmosphere we breathe.

You can, of course, view an eclipse of the moon from anywhere that you can see the moon. It is one of the very few astronomical phenomena which is easy to watch even from the centre of a big city. To appreciate a total eclipse of the moon, however, you are strongly recommended to take a trip away from city lights to a dark place. In the cities we are oblivious to the fact that moonlight obscures the stars. From country areas a total eclipse is so much more magical because of the sudden transformation from bright moonlight to soft darkness. The faint coppery moon suspended in a field of stars makes a striking contrast to the dazzling orb that obliterates most stars anywhere near it. The senses interpret the scene differently: the moon can seem no longer to be a part of the sky but rather a smaller body hovering just above the tree tops. No wonder ancient peoples found the phenomenon threatening.

It is of interest to see how dark the moon becomes, and to compare successive eclipses. There is a numerical system called the Danjon scale which is used by many amateur astronomers, but it is really rather subjective. The steps of the Danjon scale are listed in Table 1.

A more accurate way is to note which stars appear equally as bright as the moon. There is an obvious difficulty in comparing a point of light to a large disc. This difficulty was readily overcome by the Astronomer Royal Sir George Airy who simply removed his glasses. Airy was so short sighted that moon and stars appeared equally as fuzzy blobs. Those with more normal vision must practice closing or covering one eye and focusing the other on the tip of their nose.

Table 1 The Danjon scale of brightness of lunar eclipses

Danjon value	Appearance of eclipse
0	Moon extremely dark: practically invisible at mid eclipse.
1	Moon dark grey or brownish; surface features hard to make out.
2	Moon dark red or ruddy. Umbra usually has a very dark centre.
3	Moon brick red. The inner edge of the penumbra appears light grey or yellow.
4	Moon coppery or orange, and strikingly bright. Bluish tint at border of umbra and penumbra.

Photography of lunar eclipses is not a simple matter, especially as one would like to capture the colours, and colour films are rather slow. The moon is a surprisingly small object when viewed through a camera, and a telephoto lens of at least 300mm focal length is needed on a 35mm camera. Outside eclipse, the moon is bright enough to record with a typical telephoto lens and an exposure of perhaps ⅛ to ⅓₀ of a second, according to the moon's phase and the film speed. During eclipse, when it is dimmed by a factor of several thousand, the exposures become uncomfortably long, approaching one minute. Some films will not even respond to so little light. Worse, during one minute the moon moves one half of its diameter across the sky due to the rotation of the earth, so that an exposure of that duration would be hopelessly blurred.

Good photographs of lunar eclipses thus need some means of tracking the moon's drift, in a slow-motion version of the trick to catch a speeding car crisply on a photograph, where one swings the camera to follow the car during the exposure. A small telescope on a tripod can provide a good guiding system to follow the moon. Strap the camera to it, and keep an eye to the eyepiece during the exposure, moving the telescope as smoothly as you can to keep the moon precisely in the same place. A great deal of practice is needed, and it is a good idea to experiment with, say, two-minute exposures of star fields before the eclipse comes along. Better still would be to place a dark filter over the camera lens such that the full moon itself requires a 2-minute exposure, and try to secure crisp photographs of it.

An effective type of photograph can be taken using a normal camera and lens, provided that there is some method of holding the shutter open for a long time. Set the camera on a tripod so that the moon will move through the field of view over the next hour or so. Cover the lens with a cloth or cap, open the shutter, then give a series of exposures on the same frame by uncovering the lens every five minutes. Obviously care must be taken not to nudge the camera each time the lens is covered and uncovered.

113

If you start before the moon enters eclipse, use a slow lens setting (eg. f/16) and expose for about one second. As totality approaches, increase each exposure, if possible opening the aperture to about f/2 and exposing then for about 10 seconds.

The moon travels steadily across the background star field, moving towards the east its own diameter every hour, in addition to its westwards drift with the stars. During an eclipse, when stars are visible near to the moon, it is not uncommon to see the moon pass in front of a star and occult it. Of course, occultations by the moon happen regularly, but only during eclipses, especially total ones, can any but the brightest stars be easily seen. If you have binoculars or a small telescope and can hold them steady enough, watch for such an occultation and note how instantaneously the star is extinguished. The trick to holding binoculars steadily enough is to give support to your elbows, for instance by leaning on a wall or sitting in a chair which has arms.

About a century ago, when astronomers were still trying to refine their knowledge of the moon's motion, great attention was paid to accurate timing of occultations of stars, particularly during eclipses. Because the location of each star could be measured very precisely, the position of the moon at the exact time of the occultation was also inferred. This method is far more accurate than directly measuring so large a body as the moon.

No longer are occultations a powerful tool for this purpose. Men have left on the moon special mirrors which work like the 'cat's-eye' reflectors used on roads. Light from a laser is shone towards the moon, and is reflected back. If the light is sent in a series of very brief pulses, then the time taken for those pulses to return can be measured. It is a little over 2½ seconds. Since we know the speed at which light travels we can infer the distance to the moon to an accuracy of a few centimetres, and hence can track its movements.

Occultations by the moon remain of interest to astronomers for a different reason. We cannot see very fine detail in the sky because of the blurring effect of the earth's atmosphere. The edge of the moon, gliding smoothly in front of an object, allows us to tell if there is structure hidden within the blur. If, for instance, the star is double, then we will record the two components occulted in succession, so the star will appear to go out in two steps instead of one. Occultations have been used to measure the diameters of some of the large stars, as well as to search for closely separated pairs of stars. We can locate sources of radio or X-radiation by timing when their signal is occulted by the moon.

Table 2 lists all the umbral lunar eclipses until the year 2000. There are additional penumbral eclipses when only a slight dimming of one

Table 2 Lunar eclipses 1988–1999

Date	Partial/ total	Duration (minutes)	Magnitude	Longitude —at mid eclipse—	Latitude	Area of visibility
1988 Aug 27	P		0.30	166 W	10 S	Australasia, Pacific
1989 Feb 20	T	76		129 E	11 N	Asia, Australia
1989 Aug 17	T	98		45 W	14 S	S. America, W. Africa
1990 Feb 9	T	46		76 E	14 N	Africa, Asia, W. Australia
1990 Aug 6	P		0.68	149 E	17 S	SE Asia, Australia, Antarctica
1991 Dec 21	P		0.09	159 W	23 N	Oceania, N. America, NE Asia
1992 June 15	P		0.69	74 W	23 S	Central and S. America, Antarctica
1992 Dec 10	T	74		3 E	23 N	Africa, Europe, Brazil
1993 June 4	T	98		165 E	22 S	E. Indies, Australasia, Antarctica
1993 Nov 29	T	50		99 W	21 N	The Americas
1994 May 25	P		0.28	53 W	21 S	S. America, W. Africa
1995 Apr 15	P		0.12	176 E	10 S	E. Indies, Australasia
1996 Apr 4	T	84		1 W	6 S	S. America, Africa, Europe
1996 Sep 27	T	72		46 W	1 N	The Americas, Africa
1997 Mar 24	P		0.93	69 W	1 S	The Americas, W. Africa
1997 Sep 16	T	66		77 E	3 S	Africa, Asia, Australia
1999 July 28	P		0.42	172 W	19 S	Oceania, Australasia, Antarctica

115

side of the moon can be seen, and these are not normally worth the effort of an observation. The magnitude, given in the case of partial eclipses, is the fraction of the moon's diameter covered by the umbra at mid eclipse. The duration is the period when the moon is totally eclipsed.

In addition to listing the broad areas of visibility, Table 2 gives the latitude and longitude of the location where the moon is exactly overhead at mid eclipse. These numbers are not given as a mere academic exercise, for they can be used to work out the circumstances of viewing from any site.

To do so you will need a globe and a small adhesive label. Mark a cross on the label and stick it to the globe so that the cross is at the latitude and longitude given in the table. Tilt and turn the globe until you are looking directly down onto the cross. If you can now see your observing site, then the eclipse will be visible from there. If your site lies on a north-south line passing near the cross, then the eclipse will occur near the middle of the night. Sites lying to the west of the cross will see at least the middle of the eclipse before midnight, and those to the east after midnight. For sites which can just be seen obliquely near the edge of the globe, the moon will be very low in the sky. If your site lies as far round the globe westward as you can see, then the eclipse will start before sunset and the moon will rise partly eclipsed. Conversely for sites at the eastern edge of the globe, the moon will set and the sun will rise before the eclipse has finished.

The drift of the nodes is nicely seen in Table 2. It can be recognised by the change of the dates of eclipses, in this case from February and August eclipses in 1988 back through the months until the same dates repeat 9 years (half of the nodal period) later. A corresponding change in the latitude is even more obvious.

Table 3 lists all the solar eclipses—partial, annular or total—until the year 2000. Unfortunately a globe cannot be used in the manner described for a lunar eclipse to predict whether the solar eclipse will be visible from any location. In order to see even a partial eclipse of the sun one must not only be on the hemisphere that is sunlit, but also within the shadow that the moon casts. This shadow is about 7000km in diameter—less than the diameter of the earth, so no solar eclipse can be seen from an entire hemisphere. In the table three latitudes and longitudes are given, corresponding to the mid and end points of the centre line, if it actually falls onto the earth. The first co-ordinate is the sunrise point, the last sunset. A very rough idea of the path of the centre line (annularity or totality) can be gained by looping a piece of string between the three points on a globe. The listed area of visibility is for the centre line only. A partial eclipse will be seen roughly within 3500km of this line. Near the sunrise end the eclipse will occur in the

Table 3 Solar eclipses 1988–1999

Date	Partial/total/annular	Maximum duration (seconds)	Magnitude	Longitude and latitude start		mid		end		Area of visibility
1988 Mar 18	T	226		86E	4S	139E	20N	142W	54N	Indian Ocean, E. Indies, N. Pacific
1988 Sep 11	A	417		45E	1N	93E	18S	165E	57S	Indian Ocean, southern Australia, Antarctic
1989 Mar 7	P		0.83							Arctic
1989 Aug 31	P		0.63							Antarctic
1990 Jan 26	A	126		74E	71S	23W	69S	7W	48S	S. Atlantic, Antarctica
1990 July 22	T	153		24E	60N	168E	63N	139W	30N	Finland, USSR, N. Pacific
1991 Jan 15/16	A	475		110E	30S	176W	39S	114W	0N	SW Australia, New Zealand, S. Pacific
1991 July 11	T	414		175W	12N	107W	23N	46W	13S	N. Pacific, Central America, Brazil
1992 Jan 4/5	A	702		137E	12S	172W	0N	118W	33N	Central Pacific Ocean
1992 June 30	T			56W	36S	10W	25S	39E	52S	S. Atlantic
1992 Dec 24	P		0.84							Arctic
1993 May 21	P		0.74							Arctic
1993 Nov 13	P		0.93							Antarctic
1994 May 10	A	374		146W	14N	82W	42N	4W	32N	E. Pacific, N. America, Atlantic, NW Africa
1994 Nov 3	T	263		97W	8S	33W	36S	47E	32S	Peru, Brazil, S. Atlantic
1995 Apr 29	A	398		137W	32S	77W	4S	23W	7S	S. Pacific, Peru, Brazil, S. Atlantic
1995 Oct 24	T	125		51E	35N	114E	8N	172E	6N	Iran, India, E. Indies, N. Pacific
1996 Apr 17	P		0.88							Antarctic
1996 Oct 12	P		0.76							Arctic
1997 Mar 9	T	170		87E	49N	130E	58N	158W	83N	USSR, Arctic
1997 Sep 2	P		0.90							Antarctic
1998 Feb 26	T	236		144W	2S	83W	5N	19W	30N	Pacific, Panama, N. Atlantic
1998 Aug 22	A	194		87E	1S	144E	2S	155E	29S	Indian Ocean, E. Indies, S. Pacific
1999 Feb 16	A	143		8E	42S	99E	38S	154E	14S	Indian Ocean, Australia, S. Pacific
1999 Aug 11	A	143		65W	41N	22E	46N	87E	18N	N. Atlantic, England, Central Europe, India

morning; towards the other end it will be an afternoon eclipse.

As in the case of lunar eclipses, for those which are only partial, the maximum amplitude is given as a fraction of the sun's diameter covered. The area of visibility is always near one or other pole if the eclipse is only partial.

The duration is given for either total or annular phases. It should be remembered that the longest duration for a particular total eclipse will occur near the midpoint of the track of totality. An annular eclipse, however, has its greatest duration at the ends of the track. In this case, the duration measures the time during which the moon is projected wholly within the sun's disc. The more distant the observer is from the moon, the smaller the moon will appear and the greater the duration. An observer at the midpoint of an annular eclipse is closer to the moon than one near the end points, because of the curvature of the earth's surface. The end points occur at sunrise or sunset, so the sun will be very low in the sky and more likely to be obscured by cloud.

A partial eclipse of the sun can be observed by any of the techniques described in chapter 2 for viewing the sun itself. It is important not to risk eye damage by looking at the sun through any telescope or binoculars, or a through-the-lens camera, without protection. Simple filters at the eyepiece are not safe: the concentrated sunlight will crack or melt them very quickly. Much the same applies to annular eclipses; Francis Baily and other professional astronomers had safe equipment for their observations.

One scheme that has been popular for a very long time is to smoke a piece of glass, by holding it above a candle flame. Though a messy business, it can be quite effective provided that the layer of soot deposited is uniform. More convenient these days are strips of unexposed and processed 35mm black-and-white film.

Photographers face similar problems when attempting to capture partial or annular eclipses, or indeed the sun in general. Even with the slowest emulsions and camera settings the sun is far too bright, and it is necessary to reduce the light with a good quality filter at the front of the lens. One trick, which can also be used by eye, is to install two polarising filters and to rotate them until they dim the image by the greatest amount possible. Just how little light they transmit depends on the quality of the filters themselves.

To reach the path of an annular or total eclipse it is normally necessary to travel. Since the path is narrow, one must know precisely where to journey: nothing is worse than to go to great expense only to reach the wrong spot, as Samuel Williams did in 1780. The technique of stretching a string across a globe is not adequate. The next step is to refer to the *Astronomical Almanac*, an annual reference work which can be ordered through your public library. Figure 13.2 is an example of

TOTAL ECLIPSE OF 1988 MARCH 17–18

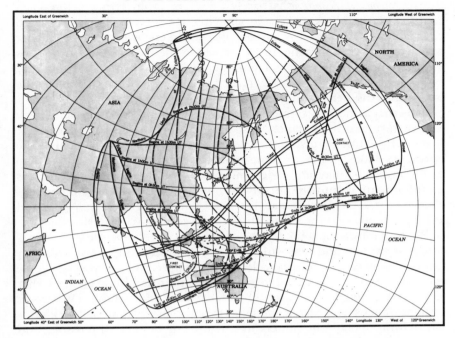

13.2 The geographical details of the solar eclipse of 18 March 1988. Compare with Figure 6.2. Reproduced by permission of Her Majesty's Stationery Office.

the diagrams to be found in the *Astronomical Almanac*, in this case for the eclipse of 18 March 1988. All such maps, this one included, are prepared at the United States Naval Observatory, in Washington.

The essence of the diagram is the central double line, within which totality or annularity runs. Various lines crossing this strip indicate the start and end times, and it should be recalled that these are quoted in the grandly-named universal time, which is Greenwich mean time on a 24-hour clock.

The partial phases of a total eclipse must be viewed using the same technique as for any partial eclipse. A few seconds before totality you may safely view the sun without protection, and once totality has begun it is safe even to·use binoculars or a telescope. The belief that total eclipses cause blindness has no truth to it, though it is widespread: in 1976 we heard of one Australian farmer who herded his cattle into a barn to save them from being blinded. Blindness, or at least eye damage, is caused only by observing the partial phases by unsafe practice.

Should you decide to travel to a total solar eclipse, the chart in

119

the *Astronomical Almanac* is barely adequate. Some time before each eclipse, better maps are made showing the precise line relative to geographical features. Analyses of the likely weather are made, together with recommendations for where the best chances might be found. One of the most reliable sources is the American monthly astronomical magazine *Sky & Telescope*, which publishes details some 6–12 months before each eclipse.

This magazine also carries many advertisements for tours, and such tours can be excellent value. Most travel agents can also arrange tours. If the eclipse track crosses much water, cruise ships can take you to the optimum spot, and have some manoeuvrability to find gaps in any cloud cover. If there are good land bases, the tours generally are less mobile, being committed in advance to a particular location. The best chance of a clear view is had by those with their own transport and ability to move at the eleventh hour in search of clear skies.

Photography of a total eclipse of the sun is relatively easy. Even a standard camera and lens will give some impression of the event. A camera fitted with a telephoto lens and mounted on a tripod will give excellent results, though the exposure times are long enough that some protection from buffeting by the wind is desirable. Whatever camera or lens you have, and whether you use colour or black-and-white film, operate the camera in a manual mode if at all possible, and give several exposures ranging from a fraction of a second, to record the inner corona and prominences, to several seconds to capture the coronal rays.

Here is a challenge for those with access to moderately large telescopes, and either equipment suitable for direct viewing or a well-constructed projection system that excludes daylight and so allows faint features to show. Can the moon be seen silhouetted against the sun's corona? The first claim that it can was made by the English physicist Robert Hooke, famous for his laws about the expansion of gases and the stretching of springy materials. Hooke observed the partial solar eclipse of 22 June 1666, which was, remarkably, before Halley had provided his description of the corona.

During the golden age of eclipse expeditions, unambiguous views of the silhouette were occasionally recorded, but only from high-altitude sites where the sky was very clear. The authors believe they too have seen the effect during a partial eclipse viewed from Cambridge, England. However, conventional wisdom casts doubt on the possibility from a low-lying site such as Cambridge or, indeed, from Hooke's location outside London.

We conclude with brief notes on the land crossings of the next five total solar eclipses in the hope that some at least of our readers will undertake journeys to them.

18 March 1988	The choices are Sumatra, Borneo or the Philippine island of Mindanao. Many observers will likely view totality from cruise ships in the Pacific Ocean, where totality lasts somewhat longer.
22 July 1990	Grazing the northern shores of Russia, this eclipse is rather inaccessible except at its sunrise end where several Finnish cities, including Helsinki, lie in the path.
11 July 1991	This is the longest eclipse for the remainder of the century, and is readily accessible. Mexico city offers an international airport and 6 ½ minutes of totality. Earlier, the entire island of Hawaii lies in the path of totality, including the world's largest collection of optical telescopes on Mauna Kea. After Mexico City the track of totality traverses Guatemala, El Salvador, Nicaragua, Costa Rica, Panama, Colombia and Brazil.
30 June 1992	Essentially the entire track of this eclipse lies in the south Atlantic Ocean.
3 November 1994	Also in the south Atlantic Ocean, the 1994 eclipse actually intercepts the 1992 track in two places. In addition, it crosses South America, including the mining town of Potosi in Bolivia and Arequipa in Peru.

Whichever eclipse you choose, may clear skies follow you. Although it doesn't refer to eclipses, this brief quotation from Logan P. Smith seems a relevant final thought:

'Thank heavens the sun has gone in, and I don't have to go out and enjoy it.'

Index

Airy, George, 75–6, 100, 112
Airy, Mrs., 101–2
Alexander the Great, 63
almanac, 50, 68, 69, 118–20
Anaxagoras, 12, 49, 62
Anglo-Saxon Chronicle, 45, 59, 65, 67, 69
animals, reactions, 96, 98–9, 106–8
annular eclipse, 37–9, 40, 66, 70, 74, 116–19
Antichthon, 49
apogee, 17
Arago, Dominique, 104
Aristotle, 49
astronomy, Arab, 49–50; Babylonian, 48–9, 63; Chinese 11, 12, 49, 60–1, 63; Greek, 45, 49; Indian, 50, 61; Mayan, 51
Atkinson, John, 85
Aubrey holes, 52–3

Baden Powell, George, 84
Baily, Francis, 73–4, 76, 104, 118
Baily's beads, 74–6, 96
Barnard, Edward, 85
beliefs, Aboriginal, 21, 46; African, 45, 46, 49; American Indian, 21, 22, 42, 44, 46–8; Armenian, 49; Asian, 21; Assyrian, 45; Babylonian, 21, 48; Chinese, 46; Christian, 42, 44; Egyptian, 12, 21, 44, 45, 47; Eskimo, 21, 46; Greek, 46; Hittite, 12; Inca, 46; Indian, 46, 47; Japanese, 46; Mahommedan, 44, 45, 47; · Mayan, 46, 101; Persian, 12; Polynesian, 46; Roman, 41–2; Viking, 21
Biblical eclipses, 60, 63, 67
Biddulph, Captain, 101
Black Friday, 67
Black Saturday, 67
blue moon, 22

Caesar, Julius, 51, 62

Canute, 65
Cassini, Giovanni, 70
Celsius, Anders, 71
Christie, William, 84
chromosphere, 12, 71, 86
Clark, David, 58
colour of lunar eclipses, 29–30, 111–13
Columbus, Christopher, 29, 49, 68–9
comets, 83
Confucius, 63
Cook, James, 34–6, 71
corona, 7, 12, 41, 70, 71, 76, 77, 79–88, 91, 96, 97, 100, 102, 120
Crècy, battle of, 66
Crommelin, Andrew, 91
cuneiform tablets, 48, 63

Danjon, André, 30
Danjon scale, 111–13
diamond ring effect, 75, 96, 97
draconic month, 53
duration of eclipses, 26, 40, 116, 118
Dyson, Frank, 91

earth, rotation, 16, 58
earth shadow, 30–1
earthlight, 17
Eclipse Harbour, 79
Eclipse Stakes, 3
ecliptic, 2
Eddington, Arthur, 88–91
Einstein, Albert, (Relativity), 6, 83, 88–91
ephemeris, 48
eye damage, 7–8, 118–19

Fotheringham, John, 58
frequency, 2, 24, 26, 39–40
future eclipses, 115, 117, 121

Galileo, 11–12

Gregory, James, 33

Haggard, Rider, 108
Halley, Edmond, 33–4, 53, 58, 70–1, 75, 77, 106, 120
helium, 80
Herodotus, 59, 62
Ho and Hsi, 61
Hooke, Robert, 120
Horrocks, Jeremiah, 32–3
Hoyle, Fred, 52

Janssen, Pierre, 79–82

Kepler, Johannes, 32, 70, 77

laser ranging, 114
leap seconds, 16
Legge, Prof., 57, 63
Leverrier, Urbaine, 83
lighting effects, 95–8, 100–3
lights on moon, 68
Lockyer, Norman, 79–80
longitude, 28–9
Lyot, Bernard, 91

magnitude of eclipse, 116, 118
Maunder, Irene, 104
Maunder minimum, 11
Maunder, Walter, 11, 73, 85–6, 101
McClean, Frank, 87
Mercury, 16, 33, 83
Mercury Bay, 36
Mirk Monday, 67
mythology see beliefs

Napoleon, 66–7
Newton, Isaac, 70
Newton, Robert, 69
nodes, 23–4, 26, 37, 53, 116

observing, 7–11, 42, 111–14, 118–19
occultations, 68, 114

partial eclipse, 26–7, 37–9, 40, 42–3, 48, 94, 116–17, 119
penumbra, 25–7, 32, 37
penumbral eclipse, 26–7, 114–15
Pericles, 62, 63
perigee, 17
photography, 77–8, 81, 91, 92, 113–14, 118, 120
pinhole camera, 8–10, 42–3
plants, reactions, 108
Plutarch, 42, 70
poetic references, 31, 37, 49, 61, 62, 65, 67, 102, 103, 106, 108, 110
prediction, 32–3, 39, 47–55, 57–9, 61, 68, 70, 83, 90
prominences, 12, 41, 76–7, 79–88 *passim*, 91, 97, 120

rainbows, 86
Royal Astronomical Society, 73, 74, 91, 109

Saros, 53–5, 61
Scudder, Samuel, 79
seeing, 75
shadow bands, 99–100
Smyth, Charles, 103
spectrograph, 79
Stephenson, Richard, 48, 58, 63
Stonehenge, 51–2, 55
sunspots, 7–12, 84
Surya Sidd'hanta, 50

Tahiti, 34–6
terminator, 14, 110
Thales, 59, 61
tourism, 41, 99, 105–6, 120
transits, 26, 32–7
Turner, Herbert, 82, 84

umbra, 25–7, 29, 32, 37–9, 116

Venus Point, 36
Vulcan, 83

Williams, Samuel, 72, 118